THE
EMPLOYEE
WELLBEING
HANDBOOK

A GUIDE FOR COLLABORATION ACROSS ALL DEPARTMENTS, BENEFIT VENDORS AND HEALTH PRACTITIONERS TO BUILD A CULTURE OF WELLNESS WITHIN ANY ORGANIZATION

CASSIE SOBELTON

Publishing services provided by Archangel Ink

ISBN-13: 978-1-942761-99-0

ACKNOWLEDGEMENTS

I am deeply grateful for the many supportive people I have surrounding me. I am certain that the quality of our lives is determined by the people in it and for this, I consider myself blessed. To have family, friends and work associates that truly lift me up makes me feel lucky and deserving.

Specifically, I would like to thank my parents.

My Mom, Linda O'Brien helped in ways I could not have imagined while writing this book. With a writing process that is more like a retreating process, I tend to remove myself completely from my day to day life to write in solitude. Allowing me to retreat for excessive amounts of time in her warm climate home was only the beginning. Her support and assistance came in many forms, but her care and love were exceedingly apparent. For this and so much more, I thank you Mom.

My Dad, Peter Sobelton and Step-Mom, Gill Lazar also supported me in this writing process. Not only did they offer ample retreat and writing space, they offered a tremendous amount of support and encouragement. I am grateful for both of you.

I am lucky to have had four fabulous individuals I have called parents in my lifetime. My Step-Dad, Chuck O'Brien passed over a decade ago, but there are few weeks that go by without me remembering a lesson he taught me, both personally and professionally. I have no doubt that he was guiding me on not only this writing journey, but this life journey.

Thank you all for all you have given me. I am forever grateful for the part you played in instilling my confidence, strength and purpose.

WHAT OTHERS ARE SAYING ABOUT THE EMPLOYEE WELLBEING HANDBOOK

The *Employee Wellbeing Handbook* is an excellent guide on how to influence best practices to create a robust employee health and wellbeing strategy. I can't imagine creating one without it. As a seasoned Human Resources professional and a woman dedicated to my own health and wellbeing, I have struggled implementing a solid and comprehensive wellness strategy—until now. This book has changed my focus and I'm confident will have a great impact on the mindset of my employees. I cannot wait to begin putting the strategies Cassie suggests into action! Whether you are a seasoned Human Resource executive or new to the field, you don't want to build a wellness program without first reading this book to implement fundamentals that few people in the field are aware of.

—Karen L. Bathanti, Vice Chancellor, Human Resources at Oakland Community College

The *Employee Wellbeing Handbook* is a must read for any health practitioner interested in working in the employee health and wellness industry. As a holistic nutrition practitioner, I have over a decade of experience and knowledge assisting people in getting healthier, but lacked the understanding of all that is needed to deploy a successful strategy within an organization. This book is the perfect guide for any health practitioner that wants to go into the employee health and wellbeing market. A word of caution: Do not attempt to enter the market without reading this handbook and following Cassie Sobelton's guidance, it will save you years of mistakes!

—Renee Jayne, Holistic Nutrition Practitioner and Life Coach

CONTENTS

INTRODUCTION

According to a Gallup poll conducted in November, 2018,[1] 70 percent of Americans say that U.S. health care is in a state of crisis. While this is not new information or a surprise to any, the problem is only growing larger and more complex and becoming more costly as time goes on. And while this is hurting the pocketbooks of the average American family, it is also majorly impacting the business landscape of our country.

My suspicion is that nearly 100 percent of health care and benefit administration would agree that our nation's health care is in a state of crisis. Since health care is a benefit we typically expect of our employer, this burden is falling heavily on the American business community. And while large corporations are self-funded and have more options to control these costs, mid-sized and smaller employers especially are crushed by the health care costs.

We have the greatest minds in the country tackling this seemingly insurmountable problem, with very few solutions. While we all want the silver bullet solution, complex puzzles rarely have simple solutions. The issue of one's health is profoundly personal but drastically affects the business outcomes of a person's employer. This puts employers in an unfortunate situation where they are fiscally responsible for the cost of an employee's health status but have limited rights around controlling that cost.

Corporations that address individual health as an accumulation of one's heredity, lifestyle, habits, and surroundings are further along than those that do not. One of the largest prerequisites for employee health is that of a healthy workplace culture, especially since employees sometimes spend more waking hours at work than at home. Also, virtually two-thirds of professionals say their stress levels at work are higher than they were five years ago[2]. These factors reveal the impact of a workplace on a worker's health.

Stressful jobs can lead to both mental/emotional and physical issues. As identified by one National Center for Biotechnology Information study, "Chronic stress has a significant effect on the immune system that ultimately manifest an illness."[3]

The years I have spent in what I call the four corners of the employer wellness/health care setting (health system, vendor, benefit broker, and health plan) have greatly furthered my understanding of the importance for collaboration across the industry. Not until considering the unique opportunities and challenges faced by each segment of the industry was I able to understand how an employer could utilize the benefits they already pay for to further their wellbeing culture.

Creating a culture of wellbeing within an organization does not have to be complex. It primarily involves identifying the wellbeing strategy, goals, and expectations while directing departments and managers to support employee health as a top business goal. For many, it is intuitive.

Those organizations that do this well incorporate a unified vision across various departments (safety, quality, facilities, human resources, purchasing, production, research and development, marketing, and finance) and strategically interweave wellbeing into the organizational development, strategic planning, and leadership goals of their business.

This book will provide the knowledge necessary to deploy a successful wellbeing strategy and a comprehensive wellbeing approach, whether you are a consumer-facing practitioner (health coach, nutritionist, physician, fitness/yoga instructor, etc.), a human resource or wellness employee, a benefit consultant/broker, health plan or health system employee, or any other type of business/practitioner interested in entering the employer wellness industry. After reading the book, you will understand the importance of a holistic health strategy and appreciate the various contributions made by all in the industry.

I commend you for taking the initiative to learn, grow, and navigate this space. Employee wellbeing is of utmost importance if we want to turn around the health of our nation. Just like it takes time to turn around a freighter, this will be a long road. It will take time and effort to navigate a new course, but the result will far exceed the struggle and will be well worth the effort.

CHAPTER 1

INDUSTRY SHIFT FROM WELLNESS TO WELLBEING

The workplace wellness industry has taken a shift in philosophy from wellness to wellbeing. The corporate wellness industry traditionally focused on the physical body. Weight loss, nutrition, and physical exercise were the primary focus of the wellness movement for many years. This is a very limited view of health and, unfortunately, what most of America focused on for many years. Fortunately, there is now an understanding that health is much larger than just the physical body. True health and wellbeing focuses on mind, body, and spirit health. Many other cultures have known this for centuries. Various forms of ancient Asian medicine (Ayurveda, Chinese medicine, yogic traditions, and others) have been preaching this for ages. This view of the whole body, or holistic medicine, was far ahead of our traditional medical model. Not only is the American medical model changing to reflect what ancient wisdom has known all along, but preventive medicine is following, as are corporate or workplace wellness programs.

Shifting from a mindset of wellness (physical focus) to wellbeing (holistic focus) has led to dramatic upgrades in the corporate wellness/wellbeing space. We are now aware that in order to assist employees in maintaining optimal health and wellness, we must focus on physical, emotional, spiritual, mental, environmental, social, community, occupational, and financial health. Each area of focus feeds into physical health in its own unique way and needs to be supported for an employee to achieve good physical health. First, let's take a step back and understand why each area of focus is so important.

Physical Health

The physical body is undoubtedly an important part of one's overall health. Proper nutrition, sleep, hydration, and exercise play a critical role in optimal health. Our society has not stacked the deck in our favor here. We live in concrete jungles, trading exercise for time sitting at our desks, in our cars, or in our homes. The majority of Americans are eating the Standard American Diet, consisting mostly of processed foods and not nearly enough whole foods (straight from the earth). Seventy-five percent of Americans are chronically dehydrated. Gallup's most recent study on sleep suggests that in 2013 the average American slept 6.8 hours per night, with 40 percent sleeping less than 6 hours. This is contrary to 9 hours per night measured in 1910.

All of these unhealthy lifestyle factors contribute in a major way to increased disease and illness. Sleep deprivation alone is linked to depression, ADHD, obesity, type 2 diabetes, cardiovascular disease, Alzheimer's, and cancer. This is why the Centers for Disease Control (CDC) labeled sleep deprivation a public health epidemic in 2014. And the consequences grow much larger when we consider that the National Highway Traffic Safety Administration estimates that drowsy drivers cause 40,000 injuries and 1,550 deaths annually. Tired employees, in addition to their health risks, are more prone to errors, have higher stress levels, and make poor decisions. They may be irritable and more difficult to work with, creating issues for those who must work with them.

Not eating the proper diet (and therefore not ingesting the nutrients needed for a healthy body) leads to a host of health issues, both physical and mental. Higher disease states, stress levels, and body fat lead to nearly every major disease in our society. Hydration is a hugely important health topic that is rarely addressed or recognized. Water intake has a profound effect on health and energy, weight, human performance, and functioning.

The importance of exercise and general movement cannot be understated. We are animals that are meant to move often and in various ways daily. In our modern society, it is quite common for workers to walk as little as 1,000 to 3,000 steps per day. Ten thousand steps are recommended, and this is a major reason why physical trackers (Fitbit and others) have occupied the corporate wellness space in the last decade. Motivating employees to move more often is necessary, but steps are just a tiny piece of that puzzle.

So how is it that so many people live to mature ages with unhealthy lifestyle behaviors? We all know or have heard of someone who doesn't eat the best diet, drink enough water, sleep enough, or exercise enough, or maybe they smoke too many cigarettes or drink too much alcohol, but somehow, they outlive many of their peers. These people most likely live a balanced life of wellbeing and probably have the other areas of focus (emotional, mental, spiritual, financial, social, community, occupational) in order.

Emotional, Mental, and Spiritual Health

In order to be truly healthy, one must have a balanced emotional or mental life. Emotional stability is achieved for different people through various methods. Many achieve this through their spirituality or religious beliefs. Others achieve this by mental stimulation. Some find like-minded groups of people with whom they share common value and belief systems. The underlying goal is to find purpose. When a person feels a sense of purpose, they are far more likely to be emotionally or mentally balanced and healthy. All the proper eating, exercise, or sleep cannot take the place of emotional stability.

Actually, to the contrary, I would ask why people eat unhealthily, begrudge exercise, or have difficulty sleeping? Why do people have cravings for food they know is bad for them? Why do people dislike movement when the body craves it? Why can't people fall asleep or stay asleep during the night?

We have a common name for foods that many of us crave that reveals the reason we crave it. Comfort foods are a great example of how we use food to self-medicate. We seek comfort in foods when our emotional, mental, or spiritual health is out of balance. We lie awake in bed when our minds are consumed with life stressors. We have difficulty sleeping when our bodies are restless from the lack of physical exercise. Just like an animal that has been locked up all day or a child who is fed too much sugar, we have physical and mental effects from the decisions we make. And those decisions are made because of mental or emotional imbalance. It's a vicious circle many of us are living in.

This is why focusing on emotional or mental health has become such an important area of wellbeing. An emotionally healthy and balanced person craves healthy foods and proper exercise and can sleep soundly. They can withstand the cravings and choose not to engage in unhealthy behaviors because they will immediately feel the imbalance it causes. They may not even know they are doing this, but their balanced state of wellbeing guides them toward a healthy lifestyle. This is how many people effortlessly live a healthy life. They have an internal compass that they inherently follow, guiding them toward the path of optimal health.

Social and Community Health

We are social beings and many of us need a strong sense of community to thrive. It is impossible to deny the importance of social interactions on society. Our families and governments and even our global economy are formed from social interactions. We find safety in numbers. And without safety, we cannot thrive personally. Consider Maslow's hierarchy of needs.[4]

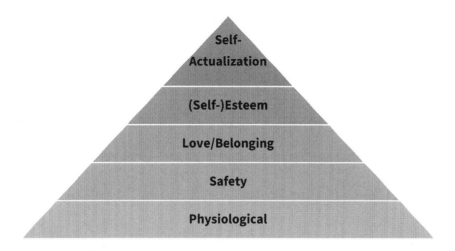

To achieve health, we need basic physiological needs like air, water, food, shelter, sleep, and clothing. Next we need personal security, resources, finances, and employment. Then we need to feel loved or feel a sense of belonging (social connectivity). Only from there can we start to have self-esteem with a sense of respect, recognition, status, strength, and freedom. Once all these needs are met, we can desire to become the best version of ourselves and strive for self-actualization.

None of these needs can be met without first building the foundation. We have progressed as a society by tending to the most basic of needs first, building upon each to allow individuals the flexibility to achieve their greatest potential. We cannot expect anyone who is struggling to meet the foundational blocks to achieve the blocks above their foundation. We must assist in meeting one's basic needs before expecting them to achieve their greatest potential. This applies to one's general health as well as occupational health. If someone is struggling to feel connected in society or has no support system, it will be very difficult (if not impossible) for them to achieve health or contribute in a meaningful way to their society or their organization's goals and mission.

Environmental Health

Our environment shapes us. Our health is undermined by exposure to risks in our homes, communities, and workplaces. The quality of air, water, and sanitization; exposure to chemicals, radiation, and noise; and the state of agriculture and climate are just a few factors to consider.

There has been a body of research around "Blue Zones"—places where people live the longest, healthiest lives—primarily led by author Dan Buettner.[5]

He has studied why and how certain people live longer than others by teaming up with National Geographic to find pockets of people in the world living long lives to study their behaviors.

The five pockets they found were people living in Sardinia (Italy), Ikaria (Greece), Nicoya Peninsula (Costa Rica), Okinawa (Japan) and Loma Linda, California (U.S.).[6] These cultures have uncovered the secrets of longevity.[7] They were able to narrow down nine evidence-based common denominators between all these groups. The nine healthy lifestyle habits shared by these groups were:

1. They move naturally (living in environments that nudge them to move without thinking about it)
2. They know their sense of purpose
3. They have routines to shed stress
4. They eat until they are only 80 percent full and eat only a small meal in the late afternoon/early evening (with nothing beyond this)
5. Plants are the cornerstone of their diets – they eat little, if any, meat
6. They drink alcohol moderately (one or two drinks per day) and with friends/family

7. They belong to a faith-based community (denomination did not matter)

8. They put their families first

9. They belonged to social circles that supported healthy behaviors[8]

Studying the citizens in these areas can give us a greater understanding of what we need to help our citizens achieve optimal health. This information is valuable to communities in all senses of the word: families, friend circles, workplaces, neighborhoods, cities, counties, states, and countries.

Where we live, the food we have access to, the safety of our neighborhoods, and the toxins we are exposed to all contribute to our overall health and wellbeing. We have environmental health specialists that investigate, measure, and assess hazardous environmental agents in our society. Their job is to recommend and implement protective interventions that control hazards to health. Their role in society developing, controlling, and enforcing guidelines, policies, laws, and regulations has a vast impact on the health of our citizens.

Similarly, workplaces focus on environmental hazards and are governed by the Occupational Safety and Health Administration to provide a safe place for an employee to work. Taking this a step further, we can see how workplaces can impact our overall health and wellbeing. Access to healthy food, sunlight, quality air and water, and safe places to move our bodies, and the ability to be mobile at work and to shut off work when leaving are all important environmental factors that impact our health.

Consider examples as simple as your activity levels in various climates, food choices in certain neighborhoods, or sleep patterns in various environments. Consider how much movement you get daily when you have a desk job versus a restaurant server job. Consider how healthy you eat when you are at home versus traveling for work.

Consider how many times you get to the gym during your regular workweek and a hectic workweek. If your own life can vary so greatly based on your environment, imagine what an environment can do to a large group of people.

If we are already motivated to live a healthy lifestyle and are put in an organization that does not support our healthy lifestyle, it will be difficult to keep the motivation. Consider an employee who already lives a healthy lifestyle. This person has a balanced diet, eats little processed food, moves often, sleeps well, and is motivated to continue this journey. They start a new position at a call center. They are offered a desk to sit at each day (with no stand-up option). The only source of food is a vending machine with unhealthy choices, and a refrigerator is not made available so the employee can bring food to work. There are no safe walking paths on campus or places to exercise, and there is no sunlight in the building. The employee is expected to answer emails even when at home, and so on. This employee is going to have a rude awakening and most likely a strong negative effect on her health. Despite already having healthy habits, this environment does not support those habits and this employee will have a very difficult time staying healthy.

We need access to sunlight, clean water, areas to move our bodies, and downtime to stay healthy. In the example given above, the environment that the employee finds herself in will deter her from maintaining her healthy lifestyle. The environment in which we ask our employees to work will greatly impact their lifestyle choices. If we limit their ability to stay healthy, we will limit their health and wellbeing. If we encourage a healthy environment, we will encourage their health and wellbeing.

Occupational Health

Just like we need to find purpose in our personal lives to be happy and healthy, we must find purpose and meaning in our daily work lives to thrive. Of course, this means different things to different people and does not mean we have to hold a position of power or influence. Finding purpose in our work can happen with any job and strongly correlates to someone's internal compass and purpose. We just need to feel as if we are contributing to a better life and better world with what we do in our daily work. Every job can provide purpose. Every job is important. Finding pride in our work and purpose in doing it well leads to a fulfilling work life. Purpose is generally something we shape versus something we find in our work.

Finding a connection between the work we do and a purpose we are serving is a wonderful way to cultivate our health around our occupation. For example, regardless of someone's position at a health care institution, connecting that person's daily tasks with the lives the corporation is benefiting will help a person feel fulfilled. Every position in a health care organization is centered around the mission of that corporation. If they are producing medicine, medical devices, or research that ultimately helps someone live a healthier, happier life, every position (from data entry, customer services, finance, sales, marketing, janitorial, etc.) contributes to that corporation's success and, ultimately, to the end consumer's health. If each worker in that corporation feels strongly tied to the mission of delivering services to the end consumer, each employee will feel tied to a greater mission and purpose in their work.

One's happiness and fulfillment in their career is also greatly influenced by their relationships with those they work with. If we have supportive work relationships, we are more likely to be happy in our daily work. Helping employees find and connect with friends at work will prove to be beneficial to the corporation as it pertains to ROI (return on investment) and VOI (value on investment), both of which are terms we will clarify as we proceed in the book. Linking employees with people with similar interests or affiliations can help them form bonds that make them feel happier and more fulfilled at work. Gallup is known for their employee survey question "Do you have a best friend at work?" According to Gallup research,[9] if someone develops close relationships at work, their productivity and performance improves. Gallup also observed that employees who report having a best friend at work were:

- 43 percent more likely to report having received praise or recognition for their work in the last seven days.
- 37 percent more likely to report that someone at work encourages their development.
- 35 percent more likely to report coworker commitment to quality.
- 28 percent more likely to report that in the last six months, someone at work has talked to them about their progress.
- 27 percent more likely to report that the mission of their company makes them feel their job is important.
- 27 percent more likely to report that their opinions seem to count at work.
- 21 percent more likely to report that at work, they have the opportunity to do what they do best every day.

Feeling recognized and rewarded at work is an important part of finding fulfillment and fueling purpose. As social beings, we want and need to be recognized. Since this is very difficult for senior leaders to do for every employee, managers and coworkers play an important role in this task.

There are many ways to connect employees in the workplace. A few of the obvious ones are sponsoring sports teams and hosting onsite classes, events, picnics, and celebrations. Mentorship programs or other one-on-one campaigns driving employees to connect are essential for occupational or career wellbeing. Some organizations have an entire role or even department focusing on this important task. This is typically called "employee engagement" and goes hand in hand with wellness or wellbeing. One is a piece of the other and they intermingle perfectly in corporate America.

Financial Health

Financial health and wellbeing has traditionally not received the attention it deserves in the corporate wellbeing industry. Luckily, that trend is reversing, and this is becoming a hot topic. We know, and mainstream medicine has acknowledged, that stress is the greatest single contributor to disease. And there are few causes of stress greater than personal finances.

Referring back to Maslow's hierarchy of needs, finances play an enormous role in the lower two sets of needs: physiological and safety. The basic human needs of shelter, clothing, food, personal security, resources, and employment all correlate to one's financial needs. Without finances to support these needs, a human will have a very difficult time focusing on the needs above them in the hierarchy.

Consider what it would be like if you were not financially able to pay your bills. It would be very difficult to focus on work if you could not stop thinking about the inability to pay your mortgage or rent. The stress around losing your shelter would far exceed any drive to be productive at work. And that stress would not only interfere with your work, it would cause a host of physiological issues, possibly manifesting in a state of disease.

Like other forms of chronic stress, financial stress can affect one's mental and physical health. Stress can cause insomnia, leading to even more physical issues. Stress can change someone's appetite and eating patterns, resulting in unhealthy eating or possibly reducing or eliminating the desire to eat. Stress can lead to digestive problems, ⁱs, nausea, depression, or many other physical symptoms. ɔtress increases inflammation in our bodies and raises our cortisol (hormone) levels, leading to acute and chronic diseases.

Consider the following:

- 60 percent of employees worry about money.[10]
- 71 percent of employees say their top source of stress is personal finances.[11]
- 32 percent of Americans say finances keep them from living a healthy lifestyle.[12]
- 52 percent of employees expect to postpone their retirement due to their financial situation.[13]
- Less than half of employees are prepared with emergency savings.[14]
- 49 percent of employees are concerned, anxious, or fearful about their current financial wellbeing.
- Those who do not consider themselves financially secure are more than twice as anxious as those who do.
- 30 percent of employees say they lie awake at night worrying about money. [15]

This can dramatically impact employees and corporations alike.

- 1 in 3 employees admit to being less productive at work because of financial stress.[16]
- By limiting personal financial distractions in the workplace, employers can potentially save as much as $5,000 per employee, per year.[17]
- 25 percent of employees say the new benefit they want the most is financial wellness.[18]
- 66 percent of employers agree that employees are less productive at work when worried about personal finance problems.
- 74 percent of employees state that they gain peace of mind

by achieving financial wellbeing through (their company's) benefits.[19]

- HR professionals reported that employee stress and their ability to focus on work were the aspects of employee performance that were most negatively affected by personal financial challenges.[20]

Helping employees to find financial health and freedom can improve an organization's bottom line in various ways. Reducing absenteeism, increasing retention, improving productivity, and minimizing retirement savings loans are just the start. Providing financial support for employees and helping to increase financial health and wellbeing makes good business sense. It also helps employees find value in the partnership between themselves and their employer. The employer becomes more important to the employee. The employee becomes more faithful and dependent upon the employer. The employee naturally becomes more engaged in his role within the organization. And ultimately, the employee has a more well-rounded and balanced financial life.

The goal of a wellness or wellbeing strategy is to offer tools and resources to assist employees with each of these areas of wellbeing. This often includes promoting positive psychology, the identification of one's life purpose, and the pursuit of meaningful interests. Different organizations will have different objectives, based on their employee population. For example, an IT giant would most likely have younger employees who are just starting their career and adult life. They are typically thinking about purchasing their first home, getting married, starting a family, and finding their place in society. A more traditional workplace, like a law firm possibly, might have a broader range of ages and more mature employees. These employees are more concerned with retirement, chronic disease management, downsizing, and the like. The tools necessary to assist these two diverse populations vary greatly. It is for this reason that each organization must assess the needs of their specific population in order to put together a meaningful and effective wellbeing program.

CHAPTER 2

FOCUSING ON CULTURE

Unlike many industries, corporate wellness is difficult to define due to the diverse approaches, strategies, philosophies, and vendors in this immature industry. There are very few vendors that take a holistic approach when it comes to the design of a program (the areas of focus we discussed in the previous chapter), and even rarer are vendors that can integrate a holistic approach in its services. By this I mean most vendors only do a portion of what is necessary to drive a culture of wellbeing at an organization. Some examples of this include:

- Online Portal or Platform
    - Health (Risk) Assessment
    - Wearables Integration (Fitbit, etc.)
    - Wellness Challenges
    - Video or Webinar Education
    - PCP/Biometric Result Aggregate Function
    - Plan for Health (Individualized for Participant)

- Reporting and Integration of Data
    - Wellness Interventions
    - Employee Medical Costs
    - Employee Productivity
    - Employee Absenteeism
    - Employee Retention
    - Financial Analysis
    - Cost Avoidance
    - Worker's Compensation

- Onsite Medical Resources
  - Biometric Screenings
  - Vaccination Clinics
  - PCP Mobile Clinics
  - Preventive Screening Mobile Clinics

- Onsite Wellness Resources
  - Lunch & Learn Presentations
  - Health Fairs
  - Health Coaching
  - Gym
  - Fitness/Yoga Classes
  - Walking Clubs
  - Group Challenges
  - Massage Therapy
  - Meditation Training/Rooms

- Communication/Outreach Efforts
  - Newsletters
  - Posters
  - TV/Computer Screensavers
  - Elevator News
  - Bathroom Stall Talks

- Environmental Support
  - Campus Evaluation
  - Walking Paths
  - Walking Meetings
  - Stretching Reminders
  - Ergonomic Workstations
  - Stand-up Desks

- ○ Ball Chairs
- ○ Phone Headsets
- ○ Natural Lighting in Work Areas
- ○ Safe, Well-lit Staircases
- Healthy Food Options:
  - ○ List of Local Healthy Restaurant Suggestions
  - ○ Food Delivery Services
  - ○ Cafeteria
  - ○ Vending Machines
  - ○ Onsite Snack Station
  - ○ Healthy Food Trucks
  - ○ Onsite Potlucks
  - ○ Onsite Farmers Market
  - ○ Onsite Smoothie Bar
  - ○ Onsite Cooking Demos
  - ○ Grocery Store Tours and Education

The above categories are a mere piece of the puzzle and each sub-category represents at least 50 other possible program or solution types. But, as you can see in this short example of services in the wellness/wellbeing space, there are vendors for each subcategory, but no vendors who cross over into the majority of them.

We have seen tremendous acquisition rates and vendor partner relationships in the industry and for good reason. Vendors are realizing they cannot tackle (let alone solve) this enormous problem using limited approaches. All areas of wellbeing must be addressed using the full range of industry offerings. This makes for a very confusing and sometimes overwhelming undertaking when building a wellness or wellbeing strategy.

Typically the human resource department is tasked with wellness. Occasionally, a safety department might lead the charge. In either situation, this is typically done off the side of their desk (meaning, as an add-on to their job description and duties). Larger organizations may have a dedicated wellness director, and the very lucky ones have a full department. However, the majority of professionals trying to build a wellness program are working with a limited budget, limited hours to devote, mounting expectations and pressures, and overwhelming confusion from the industry leaders.

There is no doubt that the wellness industry comes with heavy cross-currents of information. Even defining wellness (or now wellbeing) is a confusing topic. What is corporate wellness? Is it a program? Is it a strategy? Is it a philosophy? Is it an onsite event? Is it a portal? Is it the company culture?

And my answer would be YES. Yes, wellbeing is all of those things. Wellbeing is interwoven in a corporation's culture. It is a strategy, a philosophy, and the environment created for employees through support in all areas of wellbeing (physical, emotional, mental, spiritual, environmental, social, community, occupational, and financial). It is an employer who cares. It is employee engagement. It is supporting employees to have a best friend at work. It is a policy within a corporation that says unhealthy food is not tolerated at our workplace (and then refrains from ordering pizza for the onsite events and meetings). It is a company that promotes work/life balance. It is a company that promotes from within. It is a company that supports racial diversity and equal pay and supports its local and national environment. It's a corporation that understands the differences between millennials and baby boomers and the disparity in their priorities. It is an employer who sets up the workplace to maximize movement, sponsors sports leagues, and runs challenges to help motivate employees to achieve a healthy lifestyle. It is incentives built to encourage employees (and their family members) to see their primary care physician annually and to engage in age- and gender-appropriate screenings. It is offering health reimbursement arrangements (HRAs) and health spending accounts (HSAs) to help employees fund medical expenses. It is retirement accounts, student loan payoffs, and emergency and vacation funds. It is all of these examples or some of these examples, based on the needs of the employee demographics.

This is where traditional wellness vendors fall flat. They primarily revolve around a portal and online programs. Portals or online tools are wonderful at collecting data and using that data to tell a meaningful story and, for this reason, I highly recommend them. However, there are many types of portals out there. Some have been built to be super fancy with many bells and whistles. They might be gamified or have avatars, social networking, or incentive malls (an area within the portal where employees can redeem any incentives they earned for various types of items). Many of them are an online world of health that feels like a video game to the user. While they may have challenges or education that teaches skills around each area of wellbeing, the bulk of portals have a very difficult time engaging the majority of employees. Typically two types of employees engage these online platforms or programs: 1) employees who are already healthy and 2) employees who are interested in the incentive. Let's look at both sets of employees.

First are the employees who are already healthy. They will typically be excited to participate in the wellness portal or online program, especially at the beginning, because it is an area of interest to them. These are your health nuts, healthy eaters, runners, yogis, CrossFitters, and other workout fanatics. They love to talk and learn about things that relate to health. They would do this on their free time and truly love the topic. This is a great population to engage, and it is very important to keep the healthy employees healthy. If we look at the progression of health to illness, it usually correlates to age. Most people start healthy in life and slowly progress toward a state of disease and illness. Keeping this group interested and healthy can prevent this. Would they do this on their own without your incentive or portal? Probably, but even the healthy fall off track and need assistance.

The second set of employees who will participate in a wellness portal are those employees who are interested in the incentive. We do want to engage employees, even if it starts with an incentive. An incentive is an extrinsic motivator, something outside of the person that is motivating them. In this case, an incentive could be money, reduced health care premiums, additional benefits, PTO (personal time off), jeans day, parking spot, and so on. Many times people need an extrinsic motivator to get them started on a journey. The goal is for that extrinsic (external) motivator to morph into an intrinsic (internal) motivator once they are feeling better and realize the benefits of a healthy lifestyle. This may or may not happen. The study of extrinsic and intrinsic motivation and how individuals are inspired to make behavioral changes is a large field of study. This technique is especially helpful to health coaches in a one-on-one setting, as each of us is unique and the reasons for our behaviors are too. It can be a difficult blanket application to apply to large groups, like employees.

A vendor who offers only a portal or online solution typically cannot engage the entire population. A portal certainly cannot assist with creating a culture of health. Again, some of them are wonderful at collecting, organizing, and helping us interpret the data so we can understand how to build a successful wellbeing strategy or measure its success. However, I have never witnessed a portal being the sole solution for an organization.

Employee wellbeing is a culture shift. It is taking into consideration both the goals of the organization and the goals of the employees. A true culture of wellbeing aims at making life better for the employee while supporting the mission of the organization. For this reason, it is very difficult to tailor a one-size-fits-all program or vendor for any workplace. There are many considerations when creating a strategy.

Some of these considerations:

- Employee Demographics
  - Age
  - Gender
  - Health Risks
  - Spouse/Family Considerations

- Type of Work and Setting
  - Office Setting
  - Mobile Setting
  - Driver Conditions
  - Hours Worked (Shift Workers)
  - Job Hazards
  - Computer/Desk Work
  - Manual Labor
  - Phone Call Work
  - Machine Work
  - Level of Output
    - Physical
    - Emotional
    - Mental
  - Travel Considerations

- Organizational Drivers
  - Goals
  - Mission
  - Philosophy
  - Structure

- Industry
- Culture
- Infrastructure
- Size
- Location

- Surrounding Community
  - Support
  - Integration Objectives
  - Resources (or Lack Of)

With so many considerations and moving pieces, you can see how it would be difficult for any vendor to be a "plug-and-play" solution. A well-developed wellness program takes a holistic view of the individual company and combines resources and providers to create a meaningful integration of services to address employee health and wellbeing. But how does an organization pull all this together in a thoughtful and effective manner? This is where a seasoned veteran in the industry is invaluable as a consultant. Someone who has worked in multiple areas like employee benefits, wellness, medical, health systems, and health plans can see many tools to be utilized within the benefits that are already part of the benefit package. They can tell you where the holes that should take up the majority of the allocated budget lie and how to access the free resources available to an organization. They can help you set the wellness or wellbeing strategy, which will be used to guide your organization to a well-rounded solution. They can help the organization complete and understand the results of a culture assessment, employee interest survey, or other industry survey/benchmarking tools.

The only way to integrate wellbeing into the culture is to integrate it into the business strategy. Strategies differ from programs. As an industry expert and thought leader, Susan Morgan Bailey stated perfectly, "Programs can be cut; corporate philosophy is interwoven in the fabric of the corporation and executed as part of the business strategy." Understanding that a strategy is not a "program" but instead a "core corporate belief" that does not waiver or go away. This unwavering commitment and subsequent strategy allows all areas of the business to support wellbeing and vice versa. Every benefit offered to employees supports wellbeing. The employees' wellbeing, in turn, supports the corporate strategy. This is a true culture of health. In order to achieve this, every vendor and partner, especially benefit vendors, must contribute to this strategy. We will next discuss who the key players are in this space and how a consultant, or you, if you are doing this yourself, can effectively manage their unique skills to create a culture of health and wellbeing.

CHAPTER 3

KEY INDUSTRY PLAYERS

C orporations are fortunate to have many partners to assist in building their wellness strategy and executing their programs. That said, with so many partners and with the confusion in the industry, it's hard to know who to engage and how. In addition, most of the partners only know their limited piece of the industry, and vendors are trying to sell their select services (typically emphasizing or possibly overinflating the importance of their service or product). Lastly, there are free resources everywhere and small, niche vendors trying to enter the market.

It is then the burden of the wellness coordinator to piece it all together. First, let's take a close look at who the players are in the market so you can decide who to engage and how.

The Employer

The terms *corporation*, *company*, and *employer* are used interchangeably throughout this book. A wellness program can be implemented for any size employer, but there are some restrictions for smaller employers when it comes to reporting (or analytics/aggregate data). It's a complex situation, but the basics are that reporting on wellness program activity/results is legally limited to a minimum number of participants for de-identification reasons (typically 30 or 50 participants as a minimum, with outliers removed). So, if an employer has fewer than 30 or 50 participants (or whatever that number is based on current law or the type of program being administered), they will have a difficult time understanding the efficacy of the program because they cannot see aggregate reports. Aggregate reports are reports given to employers that are de-identified so the employer cannot see any specifics of an employees' health. (They will never see an employee's name, but will see groups of employees based on age, gender, etc.) This is to comply with laws surrounding privacy, specifically HIPAA (Health Insurance Portability and Accountability Act of 1996), to keep health matters private to the employee. The reason there is a minimum number is because it is too easy to identify who is who with a small population of employees.

Let's say an employer with 50 employees gets aggregate reporting that tells them the age and gender of employees and their highest health risks. This is normal, and with hundreds or even thousands of employees, it is impossible to figure out who is who. But let's say a report identifies that a specific group—women over the age of 60—has a high risk for cancer. Maybe this employer is a manufacturing company and has 45 hourly employees in the factory and 5 salaried employees in the office. They have 48 males and 2 females in their workplace. There could possibly be only one woman over the age of 60 in the entire employee population. Reports with too few participants lead to identification and this is illegal.

This makes it difficult for smaller employees to implement certain types of wellness activities or reporting, but certainly doesn't make it impossible for those employers to integrate wellness or wellbeing into their culture or business strategy. It just looks different than for the larger employers.

Benefit Brokers and Agents

The terms *brokers* and *agents* are often used interchangeably, but there are differences. Generally, agents represent the sellers and can be captive (dedicated to representing one company's products) or independent (aligning themselves with multiple products). Agents may or may not have the business experience to advise the employer on the best action for their specific situation, as they represent the products they are selling and not the employers that are buying the product necessarily.

Brokers generally represent the buyer. Because they represent the buyer, they are truly independent. They assess a unique business situation and offer advice on the best fit for the specific business need. Brokers have detailed knowledge of insurance products and the experience to recognize and address unique situations and needs. Many employers (especially those with a small human resources staff) work with benefit brokers because they have a broad familiarity with carriers for various lines of coverage (health, dental, life, disability, long-term care, and voluntary benefits). Also, it is frequently the role of the broker to assist in the wellness strategy and program, and the selection of vendors.

This is where it gets interesting in the wellness industry. Wellness is unique to the benefit industry for many reasons. The newness of the industry, the inability for apples-to-apples comparisons between vendors, the absence of a one-size-fits-all approach, the crosscurrents of industry research and definition of success, and the lack of established responsibility and commissions (established payments from vendor to broker) makes wellness somewhat of a burden to most brokers.

Many group health plan administrators indicate their interest in strategies to reduce cost, with one of their top interests being to introduce or increase wellness program offerings. However, some brokers would argue that their client base is not interested in wellness. Whether they do not understand their clients' needs, think wellness is a passing fad, or do not have the expertise in this portion of the industry, they are not operating in tune with their clients' objectives.

That said, there are many brokers that understand the wellness industry and its trends thoroughly and provide high-level strategy setting, guidance, and program coordination (including vendor selection).

These brokers typically have a wellness industry expert (or several) on staff or, at a minimum, an employee with this as a portion of their job roles and responsibilities. These brokers are differentiating themselves with their ability to assist in setting a holistic strategy that uses both traditional benefits and wellness benefits to reduce claims (health and disability), enhance employee job satisfaction and morale, attract and retain employees, improve profitability, and so on.

A broker who can connect the dots between claims data, biometric data, health assessment data, absenteeism, productivity, and other data points is at a great advantage over brokers who have a limited understanding of wellness to be flu vaccination clinics, wearable challenges, and lunch-and-learn presentations. The value of a broker who has an integrated view of wellbeing is unmatched. Without a broker who is an expert in this space, an employer will likely not implement a wellness strategy successfully or will have to hire a wellness/wellbeing consultant.

Medical Coverage Providers

Medical plans provide, offer, or arrange for coverage of health services. Some of the services offered are ambulatory services (outpatient care when admitted to a hospital), hospitalization, emergency services, pregnancy care, maternity and newborn care, mental and behavioral health services, substance abuse programs, prescription drug packages, rehabilitative and habilitative services and devices (services and devices to help people with injuries, disabilities, or chronic conditions gain or recover mental and physical skills), laboratory services, pediatric services (oral and dental included for pediatric but not adults), chronic disease management, birth control, breastfeeding assistance, and preventive and wellness services.

Health plans cover a set of preventive services for the end consumer, like vaccinations and screening tests. This is not to be confused with the many health plans that have entered the wellness industry, providing company wellness programs and services. There is an obvious fit for the health plan to offer corporate wellness programs and solutions, since they are the holder of company and employee medical data. If a health plan can integrate and tie together the myriad data points they receive about the end consumer (employees and their immediate family members), then there is an enormous benefit to their employer-based wellness offerings. An even stronger case can be made for those health plans integrating predictive analytics and engagement.

Health plans can best service the corporate wellness industry by:

- Knowing population health risk and cost drivers
- Establishing targeted population and program interventions
- Measuring the impact of interventions on health outcomes and cost trends
- Measuring return on investment (ROI)

There are very few health plans that do this well. It is far more difficult than one can imagine integrating the services and data. That, combined with a rapidly growing and evolving wellness industry, makes this a difficult play for health plans. However, if done correctly, this is a superior option for employers when formulating a strategy and vendor partners for their wellness efforts.

Dental and Vision Coverage Providers

Dental and vision plans are designed to pay a portion of the costs associated with dental or vision care. Sometimes these are bundled with medical coverage or with each other. The role dental and vision coverage can play in wellness is to offer preventive screenings and care while also predicting larger health issues affecting the mouth and eyes.

Dental and vision exams can frequently be the first indicator of serious medical conditions. Since we know that holistic care is looking at the entire person, it makes sense that we would see warning signs or precursors in the mouth and eyes that may eventually or have already manifested as disease in the body.

Research indicates that more than 90 percent of all diseases have oral manifestations. This could include gum problems (especially swollen or bleeding gums), mouth ulcers, dry mouth, or bad breath. Some of the diseases that can be predicted are diabetes, leukemia, oral and pancreatic cancer, osteoporosis, and heart and kidney disease.

An eye exam has the potential of identifying severe allergies, fungal infections, high cholesterol, autoimmune diseases, diabetes, ocular melanoma, and brain tumors. The large number of diseases that cause symptoms in the eyes alone could justify the scheduling of annual exams, especially for those over 40 years of age.

Many of the conditions found in routine oral and eye exams can be treated before they cause major problems, hence the need for dental and vision screenings in a comprehensive wellness strategy.

Employee Assistance Programs

Employee Assistance Programs (EAPs) are offered at the employer level (paid by the employer and given free of charge to the employee). The vast array of services included by EAPs is designed to identify and assist employees in the resolution of personal issues. This could include financial, marital, substance or alcohol abuse, emotional, family, and other issues that adversely affect the performance of an employee. While some EAPs merely offer community referrals, they generally include coverage for a specific number of annual visits, per member per presenting issue, with a mental/behavioral health provider in the EAP's network. In this way, the EAP can be used for short-term therapy, like grief counseling, rather than long-term treatment for conditions like chronic depression.

A comprehensive wellness strategy is designed to help employees achieve wellbeing in multiple areas of their lives, so an EAP can be a useful part of the solution. Utilizing EAP services is a thoughtful way to execute on some of the areas of focus that are otherwise difficult to address.

Many EAP vendors have positioned themselves in the market as a wellness vendor. They may offer a wellness portal or onsite classes as a buy-up or even bundle these services as a value-add to the client. They are, however, very limited in their ability to offer a full-service wellness program or strategy. Sitting outside of the traditional benefits and insurance model, EAPs do not typically integrate well with the other moving pieces. They are very limited in their approach, access to data, and ability to move the needle with employees' health and wellbeing.

However, as part of a larger comprehensive wellbeing strategy, they have a role, and the resources provided are a great value-add to the client. Similarly to the other benefits we have discussed, the employer must put all the pieces together and utilize the services offered as part of a larger strategy. Again, this is where an expert benefit broker or wellness/wellbeing consultant can help.

Traditional Wellness Vendors

The corporate wellness industry has customarily been led by traditional wellness vendors, businesses whose sole focus and business purpose is providing wellness programs to employers. They do not offer a separate primary service, such as the aforementioned providers (brokers, agents, insurance carriers and health plan administrators, EAPs), nor are they consumer-facing (which we will discuss next).

THE EMPLOYEE WELLBEING HANDBOOK

Even within the traditional vendor segment, there are vast offerings, products, services, philosophies, strategies, and sectors. These vendors provide a large variety of services, including some or many of the following:

- Portals
- Health (Risk) Assessments
- Biometric Screenings
- Vaccination Clinics
- Physician-Based Visits or Trucks/Vans
- Incentive Tracking and Fulfillment
- Online or Onsite Challenges, Activities, or Presentations
- Tobacco Cessation
- Ergonomics
- Communications
- Health Coaching
- Disease, Lifestyle, or Condition Management
- Fitness Services (Buildout of Gyms, Onsite Fitness Staff, etc.)
- Account Management or Program Coordination
- General Consulting Services
- Health Guides, Self-care Manuals, Individual Health Reports
- Predictive Engagement Services
- Data Management, Analytics, and Reporting
- Strategic Analysis

It is impossible to compare vendors in an "apples-to-apples" comparison, as no two vendors offer the exact same services. To further complicate things, there are a variety of pricing models in the industry. So, even if you can nail down a comparison, quite often the pricing model is different. Pricing models can vary but typically are one of the following:

- Per Employee
  - This is typical for portals or other web-based services.
  - This puts the onus of promotion and communication on the employer to drive engagement of the service/product, as they are paying for all employees, regardless of utilization.

- Per Eligible
  - This is similar to per employee but varies when certain employee classifications are not eligible for all benefits. For example, part-time versus full-time employees.

- Per Registered User
  - This is a model where the vendor is only paid for the employees who register for the service/product.
  - *Registration* is an important term to define. This could mean the employee has to participate in a program where data is uploaded into the portal or they may simply have to log in once. Other variations are possible based on the product/service.

- Per Engaged
  - This is similar to a per registered user, but typically stops charging for a user if a certain amount of time passes where they have not logged in or participated in the service in a defined way.
  - For example, if a user logs in to take a health (risk) assessment but never logs in again to participate in any challenges or content, the user would drop off the billable roster after a certain period of time (for example, 190 days).

- Base/Flat Fee
  - This is a flat fee for service.

Typically, when pricing in the wellness industry, if it is not a base fee, it is a "per month" or "per year" fee. Those are indicated by the following abbreviations:

- PEPM (per employee per month) OR (per eligible per month) OR (per engaged per month)
- PEPY (per employee per year) OR (per eligible per year) OR (per engaged per year)
- PRU (per registered user)

It is important to understand, especially when seeing PEPM or PEPY, what this abbreviation stands for. The implications can change the pricing significantly.

Ad-hoc Vendors

A recent study by IndustryARC estimates the global corporate wellness market will grow at a compound annual growth rate of 5.5 percent to reach $63.26 billion by 2022. That, with all the headline news about corporate wellness, has brought an onslaught of ad-hoc vendors into the industry. Consumer-facing wellness services and providers see these statistics and want a piece of the pie.

Some of these consumer-facing vendors are professionals in the areas of nutrition, exercise, and physical therapy. They may be health coaches, physicians, chiropractors, therapist/counselors, yoga/fitness instructors, massage therapists, or multi-level marketers in the supplement, alternative health, or self-improvement industries. They also include various nonprofits in the health space, hospital systems, manufacturers of wearables (Fitbit, Jawbone, Garmin, etc.), laboratories, pharmacies, clinics, and even Walgreens and CVS.

The list goes on and on of those entering the field of corporate wellness, claiming to be "experts" in the field. And while they are experts in their own field of medicine, yoga, nutrition, massage, physical therapy, essential oils, or others, they are not experts in the corporate wellness space.

An ad-hoc vendor of this type is familiar with their industry and delivering services and products to the end consumer and can be very useful for DIY, homegrown wellness efforts. They can be great resources to bring in for lunch-and-learn presentations, a health fair, or to teach an onsite yoga or fitness classes. But, even then, the corporation needs to be cautious about a few things.

A corporation expects a certain level of professionalism that these individuals may not be familiar with. Dress code, appropriate language or appearance, professional presentations, timeliness, and an understanding of a business's culture or goals are all important factors when considering a vendor of this type.

A business needs to pre-qualify these individuals to make sure they have the appropriate certifications/qualifications, insurance, or permits to be providing services. Quite often, these individuals are passionate about their trade, well studied, and well meaning, but lack the credentials to give expert health advice. They might be a yoga teacher in a studio that holds insurance for all its instructors, but they don't have insurance coverage for teaching in a corporate organization. Possibly someone is a nutritionist who can create meal plans for individuals, but they do not have the necessary permits or a ServSafe Certification, which is necessary to hold when serving food to the public. These are just a few examples of limitations with ad-hoc vendors, but that doesn't mean they're not useful or valuable.

Consumer-facing experts often have a common voice that resonates with employees. They can relate to struggles around health, work/life balance, and just living in a society that doesn't support health and wellbeing. They can be an enormous source of inspiration within an employee population and, if pre-qualified and mentored appropriately, can be a very valuable, inexpensive way to execute wellbeing within an organization.

Let me preface this next paragraph by saying that I am myself an alternative practitioner. One of the many hats I wear in life is that of author and public speaker around health and wellbeing, speaking to individuals on healthy lifestyle. I believe in the melding of alternative and traditional medicine, and in meeting people where they are to help them on their unique wellbeing journey. I believe in baby steps. I believe in carefully wording my responses to questions around these beliefs, always keeping in mind the viewpoints and agendas of the parties involved. I advise my listeners to take ownership of their health and be their own health care advocate, utilizing the many experts and practitioners they have available to them. Through many years of working in the health care space, I have gained an understanding of the many moving pieces involved. It is very easy for outsiders to the industry to get themselves in trouble if they lack understanding of the whole picture. This can even happen with the purest of intentions.

Many times "alternative practitioners" do not believe in "traditional medicine." They are very passionate about living a healthy lifestyle, taking supplements, practicing yoga, or promoting their particular modality to "cure," reverse, or manage disease. They may give advice to employees that counters the advice given by their own medical practitioners. They may give advice that is not founded, researched, or proven in traditional medicine. They may not understand someone's holistic health and may not realize their full situation when giving advice. This can cause issues for and send mixed messages to employees. It can undermine the efforts of the organization or various medical practitioners. It is very important for these types of vendors to understand the whole picture. This is not to stifle their message, but instead to help them understand a more appropriate way of presenting their thoughts and ideas in corporate America.

CHAPTER 4

WELLNESS INDUSTRY TERMINOLOGY

When discussing corporate wellness, there are many terms that are necessary to define and understand. Some of these terms can have different meanings, based on the industry they are used in, so we will highlight some of the prominent terms and how they are used in corporate wellness.

We have already discussed many of the important industry terms, such as benefit broker and agent, health plan types and providers, the various types of wellness/wellbeing vendors, the pricing model acronyms, other benefit resources, and the various wellbeing areas of focus. Below are additional industry terms that are significant.

Population Health Management

Population health management (PHM) is the measurement, aggregation, and study of a population's health, with results put into an actionable plan for providers to improve clinical and financial outcomes. This term can be used by groups such as:

- The World Health Organization for all humans
- Government bodies for citizens on the following levels:
    - Federal
    - State
    - County
    - City
    - Township
    - Neighborhood
- Faith-based groups and organizations for their members

- Hospitals or health care systems for patient or community populations
- Employers for employees
- Health plans for member base (those individuals who use them for health coverage)
- Corporate wellness vendors for member base (participants)

In government settings, population health management helps to set policies and programs that produce changes in health factors or determinates. Since most Americans spend 90 percent of their time within 20 miles of their home, this is a meaningful way to impact health. This could mean infrastructure to support health (street and park design, safe biking lanes, sidewalks, walking paths and trails, town centers, healthy restaurant and grocery store options, schools) or policies and ordinances to promote activity and discourage junk food marketing and smoking.

A good example of government population health management is smoking bans in public settings or enclosed workplaces. Although the federal government has not yet banned smoking in public places (as of 2019), many states have initiated laws to do this. California was the first state to enact this type of statewide smoking ban, banning smoking in indoor workplaces in 1995. As of July 2018, it is reported that 25 other states have joined California in enacting statewide smoking bans. Even some cities in the states that have not yet implemented a wider ban have banned smoking in public places.

We have also seen workplaces go a step further and ban smoking on their campuses. Even though the law doesn't cover smoking outside an enclosed workplace (sidewalks, parking lots, and other outdoor areas of a campus) an employer can prohibit smoking anywhere on their campus, punishable by actions including termination of employment.

Certain faith-based organizations support the health of their member population by offering direction on a healthy lifestyle via recommended practices as well as health promotion programs. Many promote vegetarian/vegan diets, fasting, sobriety, certain forms of body movement (some examples include yoga, walking, physical labor), meditation, or other stress reduction techniques.

The most widely studied faith-based group in America is the Seventh-day Adventist Church. The Seventh-day Adventist founders outlined "eight laws of health" in the 1860s, and numerous studies indicate that members following the guidelines live longer and healthier lives. Researchers identified the top five behaviors that contribute to increased life-span as eating a plant-based diet, eating nuts several times a week, regularly exercising, not smoking, and maintaining a healthy body weight.[21] Some of the other guidelines (which are difficult to measure the efficacy of) are to drink plenty of water, spend time in sunlight, practice temperance, breathe pure air, rest well (remembering the best rest follows labor), and seek inner peace and trust in a divine power.

Hospitals or health care systems can utilize population health management to close the gaps in care within their patient population. They can do this by implementing preventive screening guidelines for chronic disease management and tracking patients' activity to make sure they are meeting the guidelines. They can use it to lower the number of inappropriate hospitalizations, reduce repeat visits to the emergency department, or reduce unnecessary lengths of stay in various system facilities. They can integrate a platform to enhance information sharing among the various systems and departments, lowering the financial impact of repeat tests and allowing for a more holistic view of a patient's health. Taking this a step further, a hospital system can interact with community resources to assist with environmental factors in the home contributing to or worsening disease states. As an example, they may work with asthmatics or other lung disorder patients to improve heating and air systems in their homes, removing the causes of mold, eliminating pests and dust mites, and improving cleaning methods to reduce the use of rescue medication and trips to the emergency room.

Employers and corporate wellness vendors can study the means by which their offices, campuses, or other work environments can affect disease states within the employee population. This might mean incorporating stand-up desks, ergonomically correct chairs or car seats (for drivers), safe well-lit stairwells, walking paths, sidewalks, onsite gyms, medical rooms, stress reduction or meditation areas, or as we have already discussed, smoke-free campuses. This could be any type of wellness program or strategy that will affect an employee's health. The list of possibilities is endless for ways a business can help employees stay healthy.

Return on Investment

Return on investment (ROI) is the benefit (or return) of an investment with respect to the cost of the investment. This can be expressed by a percentage or ratio. For many years, business owners and C-suite staff were primarily driven to implement wellness programs to reduce health care costs, which was the typical measure of ROI.

However, the industry has evolved. Medical savings as the measure of ROI is no longer the primary selling feature, nor is it the standard reason for implementation. ROI on wellness programs or strategies has significant impact on many financial measures, some of which are difficult to calculate. Examples of other ROI measures (besides medical savings) include:

- Reduced Absenteeism
- Increased Productivity
- Fewer Worker's Compensation Claims
- Fewer Disability Claims
- Fewer or Shortened Medical Leaves

- Reduced Employee Turnover
- Greater Employee Engagement
- Improved Workplace Culture
- An Edge in Recruitment Strategy

Even though many of the aforementioned ROI measures are possible to track, many corporations do not have a system in place to do so. Take the example of reduced absenteeism. A common practice at organizations is to lump sick time, personal time, and vacation time into a pool of PTO, making it very difficult to measure a reduction in sick days. This practice has some consequences to the wellness program and strategy, both positive and negative. First, as mentioned, it is difficult to measure sick time and calculate a savings on healthy employees or wellness initiatives. Second, it might seem that employees would take better care of themselves, knowing they would be giving up personal time or vacation time on sick days, but the contrary may occur. Employees may be more likely to come to work sick if they need to save their PTO for an upcoming vacation or an already planned personal day. This could result in employees exposing each other to colds, flus, viruses, and other infectious diseases.

Another measure that is hard to substantiate is the cost of employee turnover and recruitment. Some corporations do a wonderful job with this, while others know it is significant but cannot quite put a figure on the cost. The recruitment process (either using an external firm or internally posting, sorting through resumes, interviewing several candidates), hiring process (testing, physical examinations), onboarding process (setting up the employee in the company systems, various benefit enrollments, and others by job), training process, and adjustment period (allowing for a learning curve of the job) produce a substantial investment in a new employee. Keeping current employees happy and healthy makes great economic sense.

Another measure that some companies find difficult to track is the productivity of healthy versus unhealthy employees. It makes intuitive sense that happy, healthy employees will be more productive, but measuring that productivity requires an integration of production measures with health indicators. Like many of the other metrics, we need to combine systems to realize the financial impact. Because of privacy laws around protected health information (PHI) and HIPAA (both of which we will discuss), an investment needs to be made to use a portal that aggregates both sets of data for measurement.

No matter what the measure, ROI is not immediately realized. Generally, there is an uptick in both claims and program costs associated with a wellness program or strategy before an ROI can be determined. Following that, corporations can expect three to five years at a minimum before achieving a return on investment. Just as people did not become unhealthy overnight, the positive health impacts of a wellness program or strategy will not immediately manifest. Healthy lifestyle habits take time to develop and time to manifest as a healthy body.

Another topic to be aware of regarding ROI is the fact that previously healthy employees can skew the ROI of a wellness program or strategy. The main argument here is that the employees who participate in wellness programs are those employees who are already healthy. So comparing groups internal to an organization with each other (those who participate in wellness versus those who do not) does not necessary reflect the results of the wellness initiatives. However, it must be noted, as we have already discussed in an earlier chapter, that humans progressively get more unwell as they age. Keeping the healthy employees healthy is just as important as helping unhealthy employees get better (if not more so). It's easier to keep someone healthy than it is to return them to health, and thus more cost-effective. Dee Edington has compiled research around this topic and written a book called *Zero Trends: Health as a Serious Economic Strategy* that can give more insight.[22]

Value on Investment

Value on Investment (VOI) is the overall value received on the financial investment of a wellness or wellbeing program or strategy. VOI is much more difficult to measure. We know intuitively that it will make positive changes within the employee base and culture, but it is hard to determine the dollar value, making it more challenging to justify with the C-suite, especially the chief financial officer.

However, both society and corporations are beginning to appreciate the value of the individual's positive wellbeing. The health and happiness of an employee is difficult to measure but obvious in benefits. A happy, healthy, and energetic employee is going to show up differently at work than an unhappy, unhealthy, and lethargic employee. The positivity of a happy, healthy employee can translate into many business practices that will positively affect the organization, its customers, the employee base, and, ultimately, its business success.

VOI is more closely related to an organization's culture of health and employee engagement than ROI is. A few examples of VOI are:

- Improved on-the-job safety
- Increased cohesiveness within the workforce
- Improved coworker/boss relationships
- Better team effectiveness
- Higher employee job satisfaction
- Greater employee productivity
- Improved employee morale
- Enhanced ability to attract or retain talented employees
- Reduced turnover
- Better business performance and profitability
- Improved comradery and team effectiveness
- Reduced presenteeism (working while sick)
- Increased employee energy levels

- Better employee health decisions
- Reduced employee health risks

It is interesting to note that while senior leadership is more focused on ROI, managers/directors are typically more interested in VOI. Knowing this allows wellness or wellbeing consultants or vendors to focus the message properly when talking to each set of leaders. It is very important to know your audience when presenting or pitching a program or strategy.

Wellness (versus) Wellbeing

Dictonary.com defines "wellness" as:

1. The quality or state of being healthy in body and mind, especially as the result of deliberate effort.
2. An approach to health care that emphasizes preventing illness and prolonging life, as opposed to emphasizing treating diseases.

Both are great examples of what the corporate wellness industry is trying to achieve, with the first being a bit more forward-thinking, as it incorporates body and mind. We have luckily seen a huge global increase in interest in holistic health, especially in the United States. I believe the millennial generation has significantly increased the desire for a healthy lifestyle and big business is following suit. We are seeing a movement in the organic industry, preventive health industry, nutrition and fitness sciences, and the like. We see the word *wellness* at drug stores, malls, chiropractic centers, massage therapy studios, hospitals, clinics, physician offices, and even at legal marijuana dispensaries. Everyone is jumping on the "wellness bandwagon." The Global Wellness Institute estimates the wellness market to be a $4.2 trillion industry (which includes wellness tourism, mind and body wellness, corporate wellness, and others).[23] As you can see, the word *wellness* is used in many ways and often is a marketing spin. It's almost as if the overuse of the word has negated the true definition.

Corporate or employee wellness is basically the management of the population's health, where the population is the employees. We have listed many examples of wellness programs and strategies (preventive health, screenings, flu shots, health fairs, educational presentations, workplace ergonomics, portals, health coaching, lifestyle and disease management, health data analytics, etc.). However, the new movement to wellbeing (sometimes written as "well-being") is an approach or philosophy used within the corporate wellness industry that identifies a more holistic approach to health. This is somewhat of a new movement (as of 2019, only a few years old) and it subscribes to the idea we discussed earlier in the book of holistic health (emotional, spiritual, physical, financial, community, occupational, etc.). A wellness program can have a wellbeing focus. We can also call it a wellbeing program or strategy if it considers multiple areas of focus.

All in all, the words can be and are used interchangeably among certain groups in the industry. The key is to know that when *wellbeing* is used, we are looking at multiple areas of focus. A wellness program may or may not look at things holistically and may instead concentrate on just physical health (traditionally, nutrition and fitness).

Health Risk Assessment (HRA) or Health Assessment (HA) or Personal Health Assessment (PHA)

The terms *Health Risk Assessment* and *Health Assessment* are used interchangeably, and you will occasionally see *Personal Health Assessment* as well. Some feel the word *risk* has a negative connotation, so they prefer not to use it in the description. As well, the acronym HRA is confusing in the benefit industry because HRA is also used to abbreviate *Health Reimbursement Arrangement*. These HRAs, HAs, and PHAs are health questionnaires used to:

1. provide an individual with an evaluation of their health risks and quality of life
2. provide a corporation with aggregate data of their population's health risks and quality of life

Assessments are usually the starting point of a workplace wellness program. They can be administered online through a portal, on an app, by paper, or verbally, depending upon what works best for a specific population.

In addition to participants taking the questionnaire, biometric data from onsite screenings or physician visits can be uploaded into the system, marrying data for a much more complete look at the population or individual's health. Very sophisticated assessments can also include data on medical claims, worker's compensation claims, disability claims, absenteeism, productivity, and various other benefits.

Some questionnaires are starting to incorporate wellbeing questions as well on things such as financial health, emotional health, and stress level. They can also include "readiness for change" data, which is very helpful for an employer to gauge how ready the population is for certain interventions. For example, an employee may enter their weight, which shows them to be 40 pounds overweight. The next question might be "Are you interested in losing weight?" If the employee answers no, spending money on a weight loss program for that employee would not be a wise allocation of funds. If their answer is yes, it may be a useful program to implement.

As we have already discussed, the employer only sees aggregate data, de-identifying the employee population. This is done for privacy and is mandated by HIPAA, which we will discuss later in more detail. These results are useful for employers to understand where to spend their wellness or wellbeing budget. For example, if an employer receives data suggesting that 60 percent of their population is overweight, spending money on a weight loss program or challenge would potentially make a greater impact than for an employer whose data shows that only 5 percent of their employees are overweight. Taking it a step further, if 90 percent of those overweight employees say they are interested in losing weight (meaning their readiness for change is high), that would be a good spend. However, if 90 percent of the employees who are overweight say they are not interested in losing weight (low readiness for change), that would not be a wise spend.

If using the same assessment year over year, the employer can see trends and compare the population's results to calculate the efficacy of their wellness initiatives. This is how the tool becomes valuable to the organization. However, it is suggested that employees may not always tell the truth when completing an assessment. Employees may be worried that their employer will see their results and discriminate against them. Employees may not be aware of the laws protecting them from this. Another reason an employee may bend the truth is that the assessment results may be tied to an incentive (financial or otherwise) that they are interested in receiving. There are two types of incentives in corporate wellness: participation based and outcomes based. We will later discuss the two and their differences.

Aggregate Reporting

Aggregate Reporting is an overview of a large population's health information, usually based off an HRA/HA or biometric screenings, that is used to present a total population's results. Specific conditions and health risks are reported and outlined for a large group of people (usually employees) to determine which types of programs and strategies would best be implemented in a population. We have already discussed the limitations faced by smaller employers when trying to utilize aggregate reports. They are best utilized with larger groups of employees (50+). The ultimate concern is an employee being discriminated against due to a health condition or disability.

Incentives

Incentives can be used in the corporate employee wellness/wellbeing industry in an effort to motivate employees to engage in wellness/wellbeing program services. Incentives can be in the form of a reward or a penalty. These are commonly referred to as the "carrot" or the "stick" approach. The "carrot approach" is a reward approach. The "stick approach" is a punishment approach. There is great debate in the industry as to which is most effective. Often an approach utilizing both is implemented.

Incentives can be financial or in-kind (goods, commodities, or services). A financial incentive is literally giving someone money for participation. In-kind incentives—things like a gym membership, massage therapy, preferred parking spot, and PTO—are any reward that does not specifically involve money.

An example penalty would be increasing the employee contribution toward their monthly insurance premium by a specified amount for lack of participation in the wellness/wellbeing program. There are complex laws and regulations around incentive amounts that are still changing and being challenged in the courts. We will get into more discussion around this in the legal/compliance section.

Personal/Paid Time Off (PTO)

Personal Time Off or Paid Time Off (PTO) is the time an employee is given each year for sick days, personal days, and vacation days. Years ago it was common practice to have separate buckets of time off for personal days, vacation days, and sick days. Now many companies pool these into one bucket so employees can use time in the way that serves them best.

In theory, this is a smart move. Some say it encourages employees to stay healthy so they can have more vacation days. Others argue that it backfires. Employees may come to work sick, which contaminates their office and coworkers with their illness while decreasing their ability to rest, relax, and heal when it is needed most. In addition, it is more difficult to understand if wellness/wellbeing initiatives are positively affecting the health of employees or reducing their sick days.

Absenteeism

Absenteeism is how often an employee misses work. In the past, this was generally measured through an employee's sick days, but as discussed above, PTO policies make this difficult. One of the cited benefits of wellness programs or wellbeing strategies is the lessening of absenteeism. This can only be measured with employers who have separate buckets for personal, vacation, and sick days.

Presenteeism

Presenteeism is a term commonly misunderstood in the industry. It is used to describe an employee coming to work while sick. As discussed above, this practice can cause productivity loss, poor health, and the spreading of illness in the workplace. The easiest way to remember this term is that an employee who comes to work ill will be less present than a healthy employee.

Preventive Care vs. Preventative Care

You will hear both the words *preventive* and *preventative* used to describe medical care that prevents illness, disease, and other health problems. Some will argue that *preventive* is the proper (and original) word, but they both exist and are synonyms in the dictionary. You may hear these words being used to describe screenings, assessments, services, and measures.

Preventive Screenings

Preventive screenings are administered by health care professionals to assess and reduce one's risk of disease and health conditions. Many times these screenings are based on one's age or gender, so you will often hear them called "age- and gender-appropriate screenings" when discussing a preventive screening program at a business.

One of the many strategies used by employers in a wellness program is to implement a preventive screening program or incentive. This means employees are encouraged and incented (typically financially) to get their age/gender-appropriate screenings annually. This may extend to spouses but typically not to children on the health plan. The incentive program usually includes an annual visit to one's primary care physician but can also be expanded to include any of the following:

- Immunizations (flu and others)
- Dental Exams
- Vision Exams
- Hearing Exams
- Bone Density Scans
- Mammograms (breast cancer)
- Pap Smear (cervical cancer)
- Colonoscopy (colorectal cancer)
- PSA (prostate cancer)
- Dermatological Exams (skin cancer)
- Tomography (lung cancer)
- Cardiovascular Screenings
- Well-woman Visits (including prenatal)
- Reproductive Health Screenings
- Others

It is also worth noting that preventive care (including certain preventive screenings) is now covered by employer plans at 100 percent (without any member cost sharing like copayments, deductibles, or coinsurance) when network providers are used. This was mandated by the Patient Protection and Affordable Care Act (PPACA or ACA) under Section 2713. This was a key provision of the ACA due to the efficacy of preventive measures as they relate to lives saved and improved health. Research indicates that it is less costly to identify illnesses early and to effectively manage and treat them before they progress into more complicated conditions. Diseases can become difficult, expensive, and troublesome to manage, treat, or reverse if detected in later stages. The ACA removed the financial barrier the patient previously faced with the intention of opening access to preventive care for all.

Health Age

Often, wellness vendors assign a "health age" to an individual that is based on their lifestyle-related risks as compared to a larger population. This is typically provided to an employee after completing a Health (Risk) Assessment (HA or HRA). Individuals with more risks and unhealthy behaviors would be assigned a higher health age than someone with lower risks and a healthier lifestyle.

Holistic Health

Holistic health refers to the treatment of the whole person, looking at all areas of health versus a specific condition or disease. This is very similar to the idea of "wellbeing" versus "wellness" that we discussed previously in this book. Holistic health looks at one's physical, mental, emotional, and social health. Holistic health would consider the effect of stress on the body. Our medical system has been moving closer to holistic health in many ways and will likely continue to do so.

Gaps in Care

Gaps in care is used to indicate the discrepancy between medical recommendations and the care that was actually received by a patient. This term is used to define missed preventive screenings for basic age/gender screenings as well as care needed for specific life situations (pregnancy, for example), health conditions, or diseases.

Primary Care Physician (PCP)

A Primary Care Physician (PCP) provides and often coordinates continuing medical care to their patients. They are generally family practitioners, general practitioners, internists, and pediatricians. Typically a PCP is the physician a patient would develop a relationship with and see annually, at a minimum. A few of their important duties are to make sure patients are closing their gaps in care, to provide referrals to specialists and to communicate with those doctors, and to monitor various health conditions, diseases, and treatments.

Physician versus Doctor

Within American society, the terms *physician* and *doctor* are often used interchangeably. However, within the medical community, the proper word for a medical doctor is *physician*. A physician is a doctor who completed graduate training to provide medical care, receiving either their M.D. (Doctor of Medicine) or D.O. (Doctor of Osteopathic Medicine) degree. The reason for the differentiation is that anyone who has received a PhD (Doctor of Philosophy or doctoral degree) is referred to as a doctor. This could be a PhD in economics, arts, education, law, music, science, philosophy, language, and so on. This makes all physicians doctors, but not all doctors physicians.

PCP Visit Qualification Form or PCP Attestation Form

A PCP visit qualification form is a form provided to a PCP to complete that attests that the patient saw their physician for purposes of the employer's wellness program, such as age- and gender-appropriate screenings. This form does not collect details of the visit or the employee's health status. Most primary care physicians do not charge a fee for completing the form, but some do. (Fees can range from $5 to $50 but are typically $10 or $15.) Most physicians only charge a fee to complete forms that are requested over the phone by a patient, usually skipping the fees if it is asked of them during an office visit. The PCP also may bill the health plan for the form, depending on their arrangement with that insurance company.

This form is required by the employer's wellness program so the employee can verify that they have seen their physician in order to receive certain incentives. Since this form only tells the employer that the employee has seen their physician or had certain preventive care and does not include any private health information, the employer can collect this form. However, many employers choose to let a wellness vendor or a health plan administer this process (collect forms and assign incentives).

Biometric Screening Results Form or Member Qualification Form

Similar to a PCP visit qualification form, a biometric screening results form is provided to an employees' physician, qualifying them for the visit, but also collecting certain health information and test results. Typically the following information is gathered on this form:

- Tobacco Usage (Y/N)
- A1C (diabetics only)
- Total Cholesterol
- HDL Cholesterol

- LDL Cholesterol
- TC/HDL Ratio
- Triglycerides
- Glucose
- Height
- Weight
- BMI (body mass index)
- Waist Circumference
- Blood Pressure

There may also be questions to screen for depression or substance abuse.

It is a good idea to have a section on the form that gives exception for pregnant, breastfeeding, or postpartum woman. Woman who are pregnant or who have given birth within the last twelve months will not comply with standard health metrics. This is part of their pregnancy/postpartum period and not an indicator of poor health.

This form is almost always administered by a wellness/wellbeing vendor or a health plan since it contains protected health information (PHI).

CHAPTER 5

LEGAL/COMPLIANCE OVERVIEW AND TERMINOLOGY

N ext we will discuss legal/compliance in the health care industry and, specifically, the wellness/wellbeing industry. This is a very complex topic with broad implications, and I have found that the following laws and government bodies are unknown or not comprehended fully by many, specifically those new to the industry. There are many laws, on many levels (city, state, federal). It is your duty to inform yourself of all the potential laws surrounding the work you perform. The information below is intended to assist you on your path and arm you with basic information and terminology. This chapter of this book does not constitute legal advice, nor should it be used as legal advice. You should retain legal counsel for definitive answers or if unsure about applicable laws or about your responsibilities in performing your duties.

Patient Protection and Affordable Care Act (PPACA) or Affordable Care Act (ACA)

The Patient Protection and Affordable Care Act (PPACA) is typically shortened to the Affordable Care Act (ACA), "Health Insurance Reform," or "Health Care Reform" when discussed in the health care industry. Furthermore, the typical American (if they know of it at all) may call it "Obamacare," as it was signed into law by President Barack Obama in 2010. This act led to the most significant overhaul and expansion of coverage since Medicare and Medicaid were established in 1965.

The ACA created an agency to oversee the Center for Consumer Information and Insurance Oversight, which is part of Centers for Medicare and Medicaid Services, which is in the Department of Health and Human Services.

Many in the health care industry cite this as a major turning point in the industry (both positive and negative). The law has three primary goals, as cited by HealthCare.gov:

- Make health care affordable for more people. The law provides subsidies for consumers (in the form of tax credits) that lower costs for households with income between 100 percent and 400 percent of the federal poverty levels.
- Expand the Medicaid program to cover all adults with income below 138 percent of the federal poverty level. (As of February 2019, 37 states and the District of Columbia have expanded Medicaid.)
- Support medical delivery methods designed to lower the costs of health care.

It is estimated that in 2016 there were 20 to 24 million additional Americans covered by health insurance, due to the Medicaid expansion and the individual mandate, which requires most people to have minimum essential coverage. Health insurers were required to accept all eligible applicants; premiums could not be based on health status, pre-existing conditions, or gender. Individuals were mandated to purchase coverage or pay a penalty (the "individual mandate"). By increasing the diversity and size of the insured population, the risk pool was broadened, and the cost spread among the younger and healthier insured population.

(As a side note, the "individual mandate" was repealed in December 2017, effective January 1, 2019, as part of the Tax Cut and Jobs Act of 2017.)

The "individual market" refers to the ability of an individual to shop for and purchase health insurance for themselves/their family in the open market. The government rolled out a website (www.HealthCare.gov) that assists in this procurement, but there are also brokers who can help individuals with this. Previously, an individual not eligible for a company's health plan (also referred to as "group plans" or the "employer market") or Medicare/Medicaid may have found it difficult to become insured, especially if they had a pre-existing condition.

An "open enrollment" period was implemented to avoid common responses to individual insurance, including people delaying coverage while they are healthy but searching to purchase coverage once they need medical care. This open enrollment period was November 1 through December 15 in 2018 for 2019 coverage. If coverage is not purchased during this time, one has to wait until the following year, unless you qualify for a special enrollment period.

A "Special Enrollment Period" or "SEP" is offered to those who experience certain life events:

- Losing health coverage (this could be due to divorce, reaching the limiting age on a parent's health plan [which is 26 years old in 2019], loss of employment, etc.)
- Moving outside the plan's network service area
- Getting married
- Having a baby
- Adopting a child

As a side note, one can enroll for Medicaid or Children's Health Insurance Plan any time of the year.

Some (but not all) of the regulations of the ACA are listed below; those that are bolded should be specially noted when working within the wellness industry:

- Denial of coverage due to a pre-existing condition is prohibited
- Premiums must be the same for those of the same age
  - regardless of pre-existing conditions

- the cost for the oldest age group (45 – 64) cannot exceed three times that of the youngest age group (18 – 24)
- Essential health benefits must be provided:
  - Ambulatory services
  - Emergency services
  - Hospitalization
  - Maternity care
  - Newborn care
  - Mental/behavioral health care
  - Substance use/abuse care
  - Prescription drugs
  - Rehabilitative services and devices
  - Habilitative services and devices
  - Laboratory services
  - **Preventive and wellness services**
  - Chronic disease management
  - Pediatric services, including oral and vision care
- **Additional preventive care and screenings for women**
  - All FDA-approved contraception methods and sterilization procedures
  - Patient education and counseling for all women with reproductive capacity
  - Breastfeeding coverage
- Annual and lifetime coverage gaps (on essential benefits) were banned
- Insurers are prohibited from dropping an individual policy-holder when they get sick
- **Preventive care (visits, vaccinations, and screenings) are not subject to deductibles, copayments, or coinsurance when incurred with a doctor or provider in the plan's network**

- ○ **Examples: wellness visits, mammograms, colonoscopies, screenings, contraceptive methods, breastfeeding support/supplies, domestic violence screening/counseling**
- Insurers are required to spend at least 80 percent of premium costs on medical claims and activities that improve the quality of care. Rebates must be issued if this is proven to be violated.

Because over 40 percent of Americans are insured by their employer, the law also mandated that employers with 50 or more employees that do not offer their full-time employees (those working at least 30 hours per week) and their children affordable and minimum-value medical coverage will pay a tax penalty if the government subsidizes coverage in the Health Insurance Marketplace for the employee. This is known as the "employer mandate" and was included to encourage employers to continue providing health coverage once the Health Insurance Marketplace was operational.

The ACA allowed employers to provide more incentives and penalties through their wellness/wellbeing program. Eliminating all fees (copayments, coinsurance, and deductibles) around wellness services helped to advance wellness/preventive services and remove the financial barrier to access medical services. When implementing an employer wellness/wellbeing program, we often recommend starting with an initiative around preventive care. We may encourage employees to visit their PCP annually or incent certain preventive care/screenings. Prior to the ACA, this was difficult and could create problems when the employee was charged for medical services. Now that this has been mandated, it is much easier to implement a preventive care incentive program.

Governing Laws

We will next discuss the various federal laws that govern workplace wellness programs. It is important to note that each state may have laws governing this area as well. We will discuss HIPAA, GINA, ADA, ERISA, and COBRA.

Health Insurance Portability and Accountability Act (HIPAA) – Governing Law #1

Please take note of the acronym HIPAA. The proper spelling is with two As, not two Ps. It is very common for this to be written incorrectly and is an immediate sign of a layman to industry insiders. A great way to remember this is remembering that the AA stands for Accountability Act. I also like to tell people it's "HIPAA" not "HIPPO."

The Health Insurance Portability and Accountability Act of 1996 is possibly best known to the public for its requirement to protect the privacy and security of certain health information. It is the Department of Health and Human Services that enforces HIPAA.

HIPAA's regulations are divided into five major standards or rules: Privacy Rule, Security Rule, Transactions and Code Sets Rule, Unique Identifiers Rule, and (HITECH) Enforcement Rule.

The HIPAA Privacy Rule establishes national standards to protect individuals' medical records and other personal health information and applies to health plans, health care clearinghouses, and those health care providers that conduct certain health care transactions electronically, including wellness vendors, consultants, and the like.

The Security Rule protects how electronic private health information (ePHI) is stored. The Transactions and Code Sets Rule protects how ePHI is transferred. The Unique Identifier Rule establishes and requires health plans, providers, and employers to have a standard identification number. For employers, this is the EIN (employer identification number) that is issued by the IRS and is used to identify employers in electronic interactions. The (HITECH) Enforcement Rule strengthens the civil and criminal enforcement of the HIPAA rules.

When working in the wellness field, one must keep private health information that an employee verbally discusses with you private. You are not to disclose this information to the employer or other employees. If private health information is to be transmitted or stored, necessary procedures and protocols must be followed. Most companies who have employees responsible for this type of work will have established training and policies/procedures. It is important to understand your responsibilities and legal requirements if you are working with patient/employee PHI.

In addition to the major rules or standards, there are other provisions that are important to understand. Specifically, there is a nondiscrimination rule or requirement that wellness vendors or consultants should be aware of. This requirement says an employer cannot charge similarly situated individuals (i.e., separate from beneficiaries) different premiums, contributions, deductibles, or other cost sharing requirements based on health factors (medical condition or history, health status, genetic information, or disability). However, it is still permitted that a reward may be offered (reduced premium or other incentive) when one is working to improve a health factor or simply participating in a wellness program or activity. This is where the incentive designs come into play.

Participation versus Health-Contingent Incentive Programs

As discussed earlier, employers often offer incentive programs to encourage employees to get and stay healthy. When setting these up, an employer must be careful not to run afoul of HIPAA. Incentive programs typically fall under one of two types, participation-based incentives and health-contingent incentives.

Participation-based incentives are given to an employee just for participating in a program or activity. An example would be an employee receiving an incentive (maybe a financial reward or reduced health care premium) for attending a certain number of education presentations in a year or just completing a health risk assessment. No specific health outcome is tied to the incentive, just participation.

Alternatively, a health-contingent incentive program says participants must satisfy certain health standards to receive an incentive. There are two types of health-contingent programs:

1. Activity Only
2. Outcomes Based

An activity-only wellness incentive requires an individual to perform or complete an activity related to a health factor in order to receive the reward. Examples of this include a walking program, weight loss program, or fitness program. While the participant is not required to maintain or attain a specific health outcome (meet a certain weight, body mass index, cholesterol level, etc.), they are required to perform or complete the activity. The major difference between this and a participant-based incentive program is that the employee is identified based on their health status with an activity-only health-contingent program. For example, if an employee is identified as overweight or obese when completing a health assessment or a preventive screening, they could be identified as a candidate for a weight loss program. An activity-only incentive program will reward the employee for participating, regardless of their outcome (if they lose the weight or not). This is different than a participant-based incentive program because they were identified due to a specific health indicator.

An outcomes-based wellness incentive requires that an individual attain or maintain a specific health outcome or measurement. The most common examples of this are quitting smoking or meeting certain biometric health indicators (body mass index/BMI, blood pressure, cholesterol, glucose, etc.).

Both types of health-contingent programs must adhere to certain HIPAA standards. They can become noncompliant easily if not carefully crafted. If a person does not meet the identified health standard, then it could be argued that person was discriminated against for having the health factor that made them ineligible for the incentive. This is a confusing part of the law and why many employers steer away from health-contingent incentive programs. Many argue that it's almost as if the law allowed a loophole for abusers by protecting their rights and handcuffing the employer.

There are five rules governing health-contingent program incentives:

1. The incentive must be made available annually.
2. The incentive must not exceed 30 percent (50 percent for tobacco cessation) of the cost of self-only coverage in the lowest-cost medical plan option available to the employee.
3. The wellness initiative must be reasonably designed to promote health and prevent disease.
4. A reasonable alternative standard (RA or RAS) must be available to provide the full incentive available to all similarly situated employees.
5. Information on the RA/RAS (or waiver) must be made readily available to employees.

More information on the five rules mentioned here and model language that can be used in the plan can be found at the US Department of Labor website here:

https://www.dol.gov/sites/dolgov/files/ebsa/about-ebsa/our-activities/resource-center/publications/caghipaaandaca.pdf.

Reasonable Alternative Standard (RAS) or Reasonable Alternative (RA)

A Reasonable Alternative Standard is an alternative to the health-contingent program intended to level the playing field for employees who cannot meet the requirement. It applies if it is medically inadvisable for the employee to pursue or complete the program, but here is the rub: it also applies if the employee tried but failed to meet the requirement. Again, this is a loophole that frustrates employers and wellness providers if abused, as the employee can technically "try" but fail and still receive the incentive.

For example, as it relates to:

1. Activity-only program

- A pregnant employee as it relates to a weight loss or diet/calorie reduction program
- An employee in a wheelchair as it relates to completing a walking challenge

2. Outcomes-based program

- An employee who smokes and has been unsuccessful in quitting could instead simply complete a smoking cessation class
- A pregnant employee who should not compete in a weight loss program could instead complete a prenatal nutrition course

Protected Health Information (PHI)

HIPAA has privacy and security rules that protect an individual's iden-tifiable health information. There are rules surrounding the storage, transmittance, and disclosure of this information, written, oral, or electronic.

Under HIPAA, this information is called protected health information (PHI). There are eighteen identifiers that are considered personally identifiable information:

- Name
- Address
- Telephone number
- Fax number
- Email address
- Social security number
- Medical record number
- Health plan beneficiary number
- Account number
- License or certificate number
- Vehicle or other device serial number
- Web URL
- IP (internet protocol) address
- Voiceprint or fingerprint
- Photographic image (any, not just face)
- All dates related to an individual (birth date, admission/discharge date, death, or exact age if over 89 years old)
- Any other characteristic that could uniquely identify an individual

Electronically protected information is referred to as ePHI. Any covered entity (those permitted to directly handle PHI) must ensure the confidentiality, integrity, and availability of all ePHI they create, receive, maintain, or transmit. This includes identifying and protecting against threats to the information's security. Quite often this leads to the need for encryption services when transmitting PHI, but there are many considerations necessary, such as computer security software and technical policies and procedures that only allow authorized employees to access PHI or to ensure it is not tampered with or destroyed.

While the majority of these practices for large businesses are handled by their IT department, and employees in the "HIPAA workforce" are thoroughly trained and given the proper resources (encryption email services and security against hackers/viruses, etc.), smaller businesses or ad-hoc vendors are left vulnerable and need to be very careful. It is highly recommended that smaller companies or ad-hoc vendors be thoroughly trained and purchase the proper safeguards in order to fulfill these requirements. In the event of a breach of unsecured PHI, specific steps must be taken within a certain period of time, including, in some cases, issuing a notice to the media. Seek a consultant if you have questions.

HIPAA Business Associate Agreement

Under HIPAA, a Business Associate Agreement is a required contract to protect a patient's (employee's) PHI. This contract is between a HIPAA-covered entity (employer) and HIPAA business associate (wellness/wellbeing company). This contract ensures PHI is protected in accordance with HIPAA guidelines and is an essential part of a HIPAA compliance program.

Genetic Information Nondiscrimination Act (GINA) – Governing Law #2

The Genetic Information Nondiscrimination Act of 2008 is designed to prohibit genetic discrimination by health insurers and employers. (GINA only applies to employers with fifteen or more employees.) The employer cannot ask for genetic information from an employee or their spouse. This is a concern when an employee is taking a Health (Risk) Assessment (HRA/HA).

The Equal Employment Opportunity Commission (EEOC) is a wellness regulator, as they write and enforce many of the rules surrounding wellness programs, including GINA. GINA's wellness rules apply if the health information collected asks employees about their family medical history, as well as when health information is asked of the employee's spouse or child. Prior to January 1, 2019, wellness programs could offer incentives to a spouse if the information was limited to the spouse's own disease/health as part of a health assessment or medical examination (or both). (It was never permitted to offer incentives to children of an employee for providing genetic information.)

Just like many laws, the regulations are continually being challenged and defined. Providing genetic information was outlined as "voluntary" by the Americans with Disabilities Act (ADA) if the incentive was less than 30 percent of the cost of self-only health care coverage in May 2016.

The AARP sued the EEOC in October 2016, arguing that the incentive maximums of 30 percent imposed by GINA and the ADA were arbitrary and unjustified. It was argued that the 30 percent threshold lacked evidence to support its justification.

In August 2017 the U.S. District Court of the District of Columbia ruled in favor of the AARP. The court ordered the EEOC to remove the incentive rules.

As of January 2019, the 30 percent maximum incentive amount (section (d)(3)) was deleted from the rules because of the AARP vs. EEOC ruling. However, the ruling says to "remove and reserve," which has some speculating that it will be filled with a replacement maximum incentive amount.

The EEOC issued a notice that it plans to revise the ADA and GINA wellness rules in June 2019. In the Spring 2019 publication, the EEOC revised the release date of a proposed rule by December 2019, which means a final rule would most likely not be effective until 2021.[24]

GINA complicates matters for employers seeking to maximize health (risk) assessment participation and collect information that will help them understand the greatest health risks facing their employee populations.

However, under GINA, rewards can still be offered for risk assessments that do not solicit genetic information from employees. This means that employers could potentially offer two separate assessment questionnaires: one that asks for genetic information but is completely voluntary, and another incentivized assessment that does not solicit genetic information. This would be acceptable under GINA.

Some portal vendors (which is how most health risk assessments are delivered) have genetic information–related questions that can be turned on or off, allowing employers the flexibility to include or exclude these questions, based on their incentives (or lack thereof) and the goals of the HRA data.

Americans with Disabilities Act (ADA) – Governing Law #3

The Americans with Disabilities Act of 1990 is a civil rights law that bans employers from discriminating against disabled employees or applicants in all aspects of employment (hiring, pay, promotion, firing, and more). This discrimination covers all medical exams and inquiries about whether an employee has a disability (unless it is job related or consistent with business necessity). The employer has a duty to provide equal opportunity for a disabled employee to participate in programs and must offer reasonable accommodations.

The employer may only request disability-related information when participation in the program is voluntary. Voluntary meaning that the employee cannot be required to participate, stopped from receiving any type of benefits or have any harmful or negative actions against them for non-participation. It is important to remember the ADA's wellness rules when a health risk assessment or biometric screening is used to collect health information.

Just like GINA, the ADA regulations are awaiting the December 2019 regulation updates on the 30 percent incentive rule. The EEOC is again the wellness regulator, as they write and enforce many of the rules surrounding wellness programs, including the ADA. However, we do know that what remains in the EEOC's ADA regulations are:

- Section (d)(1) – must be reasonably designed to help promote health and lower disease
- Section (d)(2) – considered voluntary as long as the employer:
  - Does not require employee to participate
  - Does not deny or limit coverage to those employees who do not participate
  - Does not retaliate against any employee
  - Provides written notice, furthermore:
    - Applies even when incentives are not offered
    - Must be understandable
    - Must describe the type of medical information that is obtained and purposes for use
    - Must identify who receives the information
    - Must contain restrictions on disclosure of the medical information
    - Must contain methods that the employer will take to prevent improper disclosure
- Section (d)(4) – only aggregate employee health information will be provided to employer (unless needed to administer plan)
- Section (d)(5) – employers must comply with other laws (even if complying with the ADA wellness rules, including the limit of incentives)
- Section (d)(6) – the ADA safe harbor does not apply to wellness programs, even if part of an employer's health plan

You will note that, in section (d)(2), it indicates that a written notice must be provided to employees eligible for an employer-sponsored wellness program. The EEOC has published a sample notice, which can be modified by employers as required by the specifics of their plan. (Employers are not required to use the sample notice; they may draft their own, as long as it includes all of the necessary elements.)

To remain in compliance with the ADA, employers must provide this notice as of the first day of the first plan year beginning on or after January 1, 2017, for the plan they use to calculate the wellness incentive. This notice should be provided to employees *before* they take a health assessment or undergo a biometric screening. For example, if screenings are conducted in the fall prior to a plan year beginning on January 1, provide the notice to employees before the screening.

While your wellness vendor may distribute the notice to employees, it is ultimately the employer's responsibility to make sure this has actually been done.

Employee Retirement Income Security Act (ERISA) – Governing Law #4

The Employee Retirement Income Security Act of 1974 is a tax and labor law that establishes minimum standards for pension plans in the private industry. It contains rules on the federal income tax effects of transactions associated with employee benefit plans, as it sets minimum standards for most voluntarily established health plans in private industry to provide protection for individuals in these plans.

ERISA reiterates HIPAA's rules surrounding wellness or wellbeing programs. The Department of Labor enforces the rules surrounding wellness plans and ERISA regulations.

Consolidated Omnibus Budget Reconciliation Act (COBRA) – Governing Law #5

The Consolidated Omnibus Budget Reconciliation Act of 1985 is a federal law that, among other things, gives employees the ability to continue their health coverage after leaving an employer. Most people know about COBRA as it relates to continuing health plan coverage but do not realize it also applies to wellness programs if they provide medical care. When the wellness program does provide medical care, it is considered a group health plan, which makes it subject to COBRA.

Some examples of health benefits that are included in wellness programs that make it "medical care" and thus subject to COBRA:

- Biometric Screenings
- Physical Exams
- Flu Shots or Other Immunizations
- Counseling Services

COBRA applies to private-sector employer health plans with at least 20 employees (on more than 50 percent of typical business days) in the previous calendar year. COBRA does not apply to employers with fewer than 20 employees in a group health plan, churches, and some government employers (although, most government health plans are required to offer continuation coverage).

Employers may bundle their wellness program with their health plan so that employees are only eligible for wellness benefits if they elect continued health plan coverage. For example, a COBRA-qualified beneficiary could not elect to continue coverage in the wellness program unless he or she also elected to continue coverage in the medical plan. However, the COBRA-qualified beneficiary could elect to continue medical coverage while waiving the wellness program.

CHAPTER 6

HEALTH INSURANCE TERMS
AND ACRONYMS

While this is a wellness/wellbeing book, understanding the basics about health insurance is important. Many of the terms we will only touch upon, but more information is only a search engine away if you'd like to understand them further.

There are various types of insurance that a health plan can offer. Some of the larger health plans are the various Blue Cross Blue Shield Plans, Aetna, Cigna, United HealthCare, and Humana. There are many more, but these names are recognizable to industry outsiders. There are also certain plans that are more prominent in various states, and even health plans that are owned and operated by large health systems. A health system is a group of medical clinics, hospitals, and physicians. When they are very large, they typically also have a health plan associated with them. In this case, the hospitals, physicians, outpatient facilities, and clinics are considered "in-network" while other hospitals, physicians, or clinics are considered "out-of-network." Using "in-network" facilities results in a lower cost to the consumer and using "out-of-network" facilities results in higher costs to the consumer.

There are also various ways an employer can fund their health plan. It is important to understand how health plans are funded by the employer when implementing a wellness/wellbeing strategy. The specifics of the funding will affect how much savings (if any) an employer will realize if their employees are healthy.

A few of the common types of funding are:

- Self-funded
  - Also known as Administrative Services Only (often referred to as ASO).
  - Is a self-insurance arrangement whereby an employer provides health benefits to employees using the company's own funds.
  - The employer assumes the direct risk for payment of the claims (cost of services/benefits).
  - This is the riskiest of the three for the employer, exposing them to the most cost if employees produce a large claim. However, if the employees are well, it can also save them the greatest amount of money.
  - Most self-funded plans will purchase reinsurance, or stop-loss insurance, to protect against very high claimants.
  - The impact of wellness ROI can be more easily measured and wellness programs justified with self-funding plans.

- Level funded
  - Also known as a partially self-funded plan.
  - Level funding offers all of the benefits of traditional self-funding with the added benefit of stable monthly costs so groups can reap the financial rewards of being self-insured.
  - At the end of the year, the employer pays the health plan if their claims are over the premiums collected. Alternatively, if the premiums collected were higher, the employer is reimbursed.

- Fully insured
  - This is the more traditional way to structure an employer health plan.

- ○ The employer pays a predetermined premium to the insurance carrier no matter how many claims are incurred.
- ○ The premium rates are fixed for a year, based on the number of employees enrolled in the plan each month.
- ○ Each year the cost is revisited and renewed, based on the previous year's claims.

Health Plan Types

Health plans are intended to cover the risk of a person's medical expenses by spreading that cost over a large number of individuals. However, there are different types of plans and arrangements that become important to understand when setting up a wellness/wellbeing strategy for a company. Knowing the ins and outs of the employer's health plan will stop well-meaning advisors/consultants from leading individuals toward higher costs than necessary when seeking medical care. We will be discussing PPO, HMO, EPO, and POS health plan types.

PPO (Preferred Provider Organization)

A Preferred Provider Organization (PPO) is a type of health plan that is more flexible than other types when it comes to picking a physician or service provider (hospital, clinic, etc.). They have a network of providers (known as "in-network") but have fewer restrictions when it comes to seeing an "out-of-network" provider.

PPOs are also known for the member's ability to choose their treatment and specialist. Other types of insurance plans may require the member to see their primary care physician before seeing any type of specialist. For this flexibility, premiums tend to be higher and it's common to have a deductible.

HMO (Health Maintenance Organization)

A Health Maintenance Organization (HMO) is a type of health insurance plan that gives it members options of physicians and service providers that are in-network only. Unlike a PPO, there are few opportunities to see an out-of-network provider.

HMOs may also require that the member first see their designated primary care physician before being referred out to a specialist. For this reason, and the inability to see out-of-network providers, HMOs generally have lower premiums than a PPO.

EPO (Exclusive Provider Organization)

An Exclusive Provider Organization (EPO) is a hybrid of a PPO and HMO. Similar to a PPO, the member does not need a referral to see a specialist. Similar to an HMO, out-of-network providers are not covered. This health plan is a good option for those who might want to see an in-network specialist without a referral.

POS (Point-of-Service)

A Point-of-Service plan is similar to an EPO, as it is also a hybrid of a PPO and HMO. Similar to an HMO, the member is required to first see their primary care physician, who will refer them to a specialist. But, similar to a PPO, in-network providers will be less expensive then out-of-network providers, but out-of-network providers are still covered at a lesser cost.

Wellness-focused Health Plans

There are other types of health plans that are tailored to promote healthy lifestyles and reward those living in a healthy way. The plans encourage individuals to take charge of their health and put a spotlight on one's current health status. If someone is deemed healthy (based on plan design and goals outlined) and completes the necessary requirements, they will receive lower out-of-pocket costs for their medical expenses.

An example of what an enrolled individual has to do to qualify for enhanced coverage, with lower out-of-pocket costs:

- Go see their PCP (primary care physician)
- Have the PCP complete a form confirming they are within guidelines for:
  - Body Mass Index (BMI)
  - Blood Pressure
  - Blood Sugar (glucose)
  - Cholesterol
  - Tobacco Use
  - Other Markers (for example, depression)
- Complete an HRA (Health Risk Assessment)

If the individual meets all criteria, they will be offered the same health plan, but with lower copays, deductibles, and coinsurance.

These types of health plans are a nice way to add a wellness component to a health plan, while lessening the administrative burden of the employer. Employees (and spouses, if applicable) are required to engage with their primary care physician on an annual basis, which helps set the stage for annual monitoring and age/gender-appropriate screenings. In addition, a member is held accountable for keeping their biometrics and health indicators in line with healthy standards, leading to an overall healthier lifestyle and highlighting the importance of healthy behaviors.

HSA-Qualified High Deductible Health Plan (HDHP)

High Deductible Health Plans (HDHP) reduce the member's monthly premiums but have a higher deductible than a traditional insurance plan. This means the member pays more of their health care costs (deductible) before the insurance plan starts to pay for any covered services except preventive care.

The 2019 IRS limits for an HDHP is a deductible of at least $1,350 for an individual or $2,700 for a family (two or more covered members). The total annual out-of-pocket expenses cannot be more than $6,750 for an individual or $13,500 for a family. These expenses include a member's deductibles, coinsurance, and copayments. One benefit of HDHPs is that they may be combined with a Health Savings Account (HSA), which allows members to pay for certain medical expenses with money that is free of federal tax.

Health Savings Account (HSA)

A Health Savings Account is a personal bank account that can be used only for (qualified) health expenses. To be eligible, one must be enrolled in an HDHP (high deductible health plan), which qualifies them to put tax-free money into the account, up to $3,500 for a single and $7,000 for a family (2019 contribution limits). This limit has increased annually over the years and most likely will continue to do so.

In addition to being enrolled in an HSA-qualified HDHP, the individual must meet other criteria to be eligible to make HSA contributions. He or she cannot be covered by a non-HSA-qualified health plan (which includes a "general purpose" health flexible spending account, Medicare, and Medicaid), nor be claimed as a dependent on someone else's tax return. In addition, he or she cannot have received Veteran's Administration medical and/or prescription drug benefits for a non-service-related disability or certain Indian Health Services benefits within the last three months. It is always up to the account holder to make sure he or she is eligible to make HSA contributions on a monthly basis, and not the employer's or the HSA administrator's responsibility.

An individual contributes to the HSA and owns the funds in the account until used. They would take the funds if they leave a job. The account can accrue interest, and the individual may be able to invest a portion of the funds, similar to a 401(k) retirement savings account. The account rolls over (or never forfeits). Again, it is a savings account, used toward health spending, that is the individual's full property.

Health Reimbursement Arrangement (HRA)

A Health Reimbursement Arrangement is an employer-funded, IRS-approved health benefit used to reimburse employees for qualified medical expenses not covered by the health plan. Unlike HSAs, which can only be used with HDHPs, HRAs can be used with all types of health plans.

Unlike an HSA, the employer owns the funds. So, if an employee leaves the job, the money defaults back to the employer. Unlike HSAs, this money does not accrue interest.

It is worth noting the dual use of the acronym HRA in the world of employee benefits or human resources. HRA can stand for a health reimbursement arrangement or a health risk assessment, which is a term we have already discussed and is typically used in a wellness program.

Flexible Spending Account (FSA)

A Flexible Spending Account (FSA) is similar to an HSA (which someone is eligible for only with an HSA-qualified High Deductible Health Plan) but can be paired with other types of health plans, has a lower contribution limit ($2,700 for 2019), and does not roll over in its entirety (if at all). This means that the individual must use the money in the account toward qualified health expenses incurred in that plan year or risk losing the money.

In some cases, however, the employer's Section 125 plan (which governs pre-tax contributions, including FSAs) may permit FSA participants to carry over up to $500 from one plan year to the next. If the plan does not permit this "roll over," it may allow a "grace period," which permits the FSA participant to use FSA funds remaining in one plan year for qualified expenses incurred during the first two and a half months of the subsequent plan year. However, a Section 125 plan cannot offer both the "roll over" and the "grace period." It may offer one, or neither, to participants.

In addition, some employers choose to offer a "limited purpose" health FSA to employees enrolling in an HSA-qualified HDHP. In this type of FSA, only eligible dental and vision charges, and medical expenses incurred after the annual HDHP deductible is satisfied, are eligible for reimbursement/payment. In this way, the individual can maintain eligibility to contribute to an HSA, because the "limited purpose" health FSA cannot be used to pay medical expenses before the HDHP's deductible is reached.

Diabetes Prevention Program (DPP)

A Diabetes Prevention Program (DPP) is sometimes offered by a health/wellness vendor or health plan as a way to reduce costs and reverse/manage type 2 diabetes in a large population. The DPP started as a major clinical trial conducted by the National Institute of Diabetes and Digestive and Kidney Diseases that revealed "people who are at high risk for type 2 diabetes can prevent or delay the disease by losing a modest amount of weight through lifestyle changes (dietary changes and increased physical activity). Taking metformin, a safe and effective generic medicine to treat diabetes, was also found to prevent the disease, though to a lesser degree."[25]

There was a ten-year and fifteen-year follow-up study to the DPP, labeled the Diabetes Prevention Program Outcomes Study (DPPOS), which followed the surviving DPP participants. The DPPOS was designed to examine the longer-term impact of the original treatment interventions. Results of the DPPOS indicate that the effects of the DPP have persisted for years. The lifestyle-changes participants continued to have a delay in the development of diabetes by 34 percent overall and ages 60 and older had a delay in the development of diabetes by 49 percent (compared with those that took the placebo).

At the fifteen-year follow up, the lifestyle-changes participants continued to have a delay in the development of diabetes by 27 percent (compared with participants who took a placebo).[26]

The implications of this study are strongly indicative of the importance of a healthy lifestyle in managing/reversing type 2 diabetes. Following the guidelines of the study, vendors are successful in teaching lifestyle changes to high-risk individuals. A health plan may offer this free of charge in an effort to reduce costs.

Care Management

Care management is commonly discussed in the health plan setting. It is an umbrella term that includes activities that are meant to increase patient care and reduce the need for medical services by helping people manage their chronic health conditions. Care managers connect patients with resources that help them to be their healthiest, find in-network physicians or specialists, navigate the health system, and coordinate care, all in an effort to manage conditions like heart disease, hypertension, diabetes, asthma, arthritis, and COPD.

Medication Therapy Management

Medication therapy management is a program, typically initiated by a health plan, that helps individuals with chronic conditions manage their medication(s). Patients are educated so they can understand the drugs they are prescribed, control their costs, and maximize their results. Medication problems (efficacy, side effects, abuse, etc.) are meant to be eliminated or reduced with medication therapy management.

Health Plan Design

Health insurance coverage includes many types of variables, including administrative features, cost sharing features, provider limitations/exclusions, eligibility, scope of services, and others that impact the utilization and cost of coverage.

Other Insurance Types and Terms

When discussing employee benefits, we are not only referring to health plans and some of the benefits outlined in the previous chapter. Additional benefits could include any of the following:

- Telemedicine – Virtual medical care. Telemedicine allows a patient and physician to communicate via technology (video typically), which increases the ability for both to overcome distance barriers as well as specialty access. Some insurance companies/group health plans cover this benefit, others do not.
- Disability Insurance – There are two types of disability insurance, which work best in tandem and can either be employer paid/subsidized or employee paid:
  - Short-Term Disability (often referred to as STD) – replaces a portion of an employee's earnings for a short period of time (generally three to six months).

- Long-Term Disability (often referred to as LTD) – replaces a portion of an employee's monthly earnings for a long period of time (possibly up to the individual's Social Security Normal Retirement Age, if the individual continues to satisfy the plan's definition of disability). It does not kick in immediately. There is an elimination period of at least three months, which is why short-term disability is recommended.

- Life Insurance – this could be employer provided/paid/subsidized or offered as an employee-paid benefit, which would make it a voluntary benefit.

- Voluntary Benefits – these are typically paid by the employee, but at a lesser price than they would pay without the group purchase discount that can be achieved through the employer. Examples include (but are not limited to):
  - Supplemental Critical Illness Insurance
  - Pet Insurance
  - Auto Insurance
  - Homeowners Insurance
  - Accident Insurance
  - Financial Counseling
  - Identify Theft Coverage
  - Student Loan Repayment
  - Legal Services
  - Personal Travel Insurance
  - Concierge Services
  - Retail Discounts (cell phone, travel services, etc.)
  - Corporate Wellness Programs – although this is typically employer paid, it can be an employee-paid benefit or portions of it can be employee paid. Examples of wellness activities that might be charged back to employees:

- Flu shot fee
- Onsite massage therapy
- Onsite vitamin therapy (example: B12 shots administered by a medical professional onsite)
- Onsite classes (fitness, yoga, meditation, etc.)

CHAPTER 7

INDUSTRY INFLUENCERS

A big part of understanding how to develop and implement a corporate wellness or wellbeing strategy is learning the industry landscape. You have learned a lot in this book, but the industry is in a constant state of evolution and it is important to keep up with the latest research, as well as the industry best practices. Especially if you are a holistic practitioner, you may feel you intuitively know how to help people get healthy. However, learning and following research-based practices, as well as setting goals and measuring them, are not only necessary in corporate America, it's the only way to properly execute a wellness or wellbeing strategy. Once you are planning the tactical details or programs within that strategy, you will be able to incorporate your own unique spin on industry best practices to change lives.

There are many resources that will help you do this. In this chapter, I will outline some of the major influencers in the industry and what they are all about. We will discuss national and state organizations, local and community resources, industry authors, researchers, best practices, and well-known industry books.

National Organizations

A few of the national organizations that provide research, studies, white papers, education, conferences, and trainings around corporate wellness or wellbeing are:

- Health Enhancement Research Organization (HERO)
- National Wellness Institute (NWI)
- Wellness Council of America (WELCOA)

- Art & Science of Health Promotion Institute
- National Business Group on Health (NBGH)
- International Corporate Health Leadership Council (ICHLC)
- Centers for Disease Control (CDC)
  - Workplace Health Promotion
  - National Institute for Occupational Safety & Health (NIOSH)
- Gallup
- Global Wellness Institute (GWI)

It is important if you are in the corporate wellness industry to know who these groups are and what their high-level mission and role is in the industry. This will not only educate you on the industry but will give you more clout with industry experts, benefit brokers, and employers. Sign up for their newsletters; watch their websites; attend their webinars, meetings, and conferences; read their whitepapers, research studies, and articles; complete their surveys, scorecards, and benchmarking tools to better understand the industry and what is available to you or your client.

Health Enhancement Research Organization (HERO)

HERO is a national nonprofit dedicated to identifying and sharing best practices in the field of workplace health and wellbeing to improve the health and wellbeing of workers, their spouses, dependents, and retirees. Their website provides much detail on their services and philosophy. It was established to create and distribute leadership, research, policy, and strategies that advance workplace health and wellbeing practices. HERO provides networking opportunities, as well as webinars, an annual conference, think tank opportunities, research, and industry awards and is possibly most well known for their "Health and Well-being Best Practices Scorecard in Collaboration with Mercer© (HERO Scorecard)."

As described on HERO's website, "The HERO Scorecard is designed to help organizations learn about best practices for promoting workplace health and well-being, and to discover opportunities to improve and measure progress over time. Developed in consultation with leading authorities on population health and well-being, this industry leading tool provides you with an instant assessment of how your program stacks up to others in the national Scorecard database... The HERO Scorecard asks detailed questions about employers' program design, administration, and experience, and then assigns respondents an overall score out of a possible 200 points."[27]

The Scorecard is a free online assessment tool that can be very helpful for organizations to complete. Merely the practice of completing the Scorecard alone will be a useful exercise as it helps organizations understand how they compare to others as it relates to health and wellbeing programs or strategies. It is offered as an online assessment tool, but also has a PDF that can be downloaded and completed prior to submitting the final version online.

The benefit to completing an assessment like this is trifold:

1. The Scorecard has a broad range of possible health and well-being best practices and innovative methods to achieve the varied goals of a health and wellbeing strategy. There are multiple sections that provide components of best-in-class wellbeing programs or strategies and, by taking the assessment, an organization will understand what is available and possible. An organization taking the Scorecard can use the results to help build their own tailored roadmap and strategy moving forward. The Scorecard will help identify gaps in strategy and make it clearer what needs to be done in the future.

2. The Scorecard will help an organization benchmark where they are in line with their industry competitors. (Free benchmarking is available for the manufacturing, health care, and higher education industry sectors. Additional benchmark reports are

91

available for a fee.) Many organizations allocate a substantial amount of money for health and wellbeing as a tool for recruiting and retaining top industry talent, so it is important to understand where they compare to the rest of their industry.

3. Lastly, completing the Scorecard assists HERO in the development of their data, which helps move the industry forward with information regarding best practices. We are all in this together. The more we share data and collaborate, the faster we will advance the industry and the health of our population.

National Wellness Institute (NWI)

The National Wellness Institute (NWI) is a membership-based organization that provides webinars, continuing-education credits, connection with other professionals, best practices, professional publications, wellness tools, and resources, but it might be best known for its Certified Wellness Practitioner Course. The NWI also puts on an annual National Wellness Conference that provides networking and education opportunities and certification programs.

As stated on their website, "Founded in 1977, the National Wellness Institute, Inc. (NWI) was formed to realize the mission of providing health promotion and wellness professionals unparalleled resources and services that fuel professional and personal growth. This mission continues to drive the National Wellness Institute and forms the basis for the annual National Wellness Conference, the most highly acclaimed professional conference in health and wellness."[28]

Similar to what was outlined earlier in this book, the NWI focuses on six dimensions of wellness (physical, intellectual, emotional, spiritual, social, and occupational), which were developed by Dr. Bill Hettler, co-founder of NWI. This interdependent model provides the categories from which NWI derives its resources and services. NWI offers free resources and tools to assist wellness consultants, professionals, and coaches in opening a dialogue with their clients or employees about their personal fulfillment within each of the six dimensions of wellness.

WELCOA (Wellness Council of America)

WELCOA is also a membership-based organization that offers trainings and resources in the workplace wellness industry. As described on their website, a WELCOA membership "provides training and tools you need to change organizational culture, increase engagement, contain costs and improve the lives of your employees. Ideal for workplace wellness and human resource professionals, benefit consultants and brokers—our solution encourages organizations to fuse knowledge and engage all team members to design your own highly personalized approach."[29]

WELCOA has a Well Workplace Checklist™ that can help an organization measure their alignment with WELCOA's 7 Benchmarks™ and strategic initiatives. They offer a certificate course that allows a practitioner to build the skills needed to design, implement, and sustain successful employee wellness initiatives. They also have an award program that recognizes employers that protect and enhance the health and wellbeing of their employees.

WELCOA's resources are plentiful and include:

- Articles
- Career Development
- Case Studies
- Certification Course
- Employee Education Tools
- Employee Health Bulletins
- Exclusive Benefits
- Expert Interviews

- Incentive Campaigns
- Infographics
- Member Spotlights
- Planning Templates
- Podcasts
- Presentations
- Quick Guides
- Sample Policies
- Sample Surveys
- Summit Materials
- Webinars
- White Papers

These resources are valuable to both consultants and employers, providing many necessary resources that would take much time and expense to create.

Art & Science of Health Promotion Institute

The Art & Science of Health Promotion Institute states its goal is "to improve the effectiveness of health promotion programs provided to people in the United States and the world by applying what we have learned from research and practice to improve outcomes. We do this in workplace, clinical and commercial spheres through consulting, collaborations, public speaking, and conferences. Focusing our work on this goal will help us achieve our underlying vision of enhancing health by helping people improve lifestyle practices that prevent disease and enhance quality of life and make the organizations they serve more effective."[30]

They are committed to sharing resources at no cost wherever possible and encourage "paying it forward" when utilizing their free resources by asking recipients to help someone else with an unexpected kindness.

They serve numerous groups with an interest in promoting health at the workplace, such as:

1. Employers - Helping employers launch new programs that enhance health and advance organization goals, evaluate the impact of their existing programs, and refocus programs to achieve better outcomes.
2. Health Promotion Providers - Helping providers improve the scientific validity and effective implementation of their services.
3. Hospitals - Helping hospitals integrate health promotion concepts into patient care, staff and employee benefits, and community outreach.
4. Global - Forming international collaborations that advance policy and practice and stimulate cross-cultural learning.

They offer free PDF books, white papers, and planning tools. Two of their planning tools are:

1. WikiWIT - An open access collaborative development toolkit to help guide employers on the three most common questions about their wellness incentives:
   a. How big should they be?
   b. What are the most appropriate cut points?
   c. How should they be paid for?
2. SmokingPaST – A smoking prevalence, savings, and treatment framework tool designed to estimate the impact of investments in tobacco treatment programs on health and medical cost savings.

You may join their mailing list on their website to receive updates about webinars, books, and other resources from the Art & Science of Health Promotion Institute.

National Business Group on Health (NBGH)

The National Business Group on Health (NBGH) is a member-based organization whose goals are to help corporations optimize business performance and save time and money through health improvement and health care management initiatives. The NBGH addresses challenges facing employers with a collection of services and benefits, as outlined on their website, to include "health and benefits trends and innovations, holistic well-being, optimized performance and productivity, employee engagement, the changing health care delivery system, specialty pharmacy and health policy issues." Membership includes access to all their "data, resources, benchmarking, networking, webinars and employer summits."[31]

While the membership fee is high, so is their value. The majority of their members are large Fortune 500–types of companies, but they also have memberships for health industry partners (e.g., consulting firms, insurance companies, health plans). For those who cannot afford an annual membership, the NBGH offers some benchmarking data, tools, and resources to the community via their website.

International Corporate Health Leadership Council (ICHLC)

The International Corporate Health Leadership Council (ICHLC) is a nonprofit 501(c)(6) foundation established in 2012 whose objective is to drive standards and policies that result in reducing risk and improving the delivery of health care to international travelers, expatriates, and employees.

ICHLC produces reviews of the latest health trends pertinent to global enterprises and provides key recommendations for benchmarking and best practice identification that is shared with policy makers and influencers. On an annual basis, ICHLC publishes a detailed report that qualifies, benchmarks, and promotes the best science and practices in international corporate employee health.

Centers for Disease Control (CDC) – Workplace Health Promotion

The CDC, through the Workplace Health Program, works with state health agencies, academic institutions, employers, national employer groups and coalitions, and other key groups to develop, set up, and promote effective strategies for improving health in the work environment.

There are numerous resources on their website:[32]

- Workplace Health Resource Center

  The CDC Workplace Health Resource Center has searchable, research-based tools and resources to help employers develop or expand a workplace health promotion program that supports their employees' physical, mental, emotional, and financial wellbeing.

- Workplace Health Model

  The CDC Workplace Health Model is a comprehensive health approach with interventions that address multiple risk factors and health conditions at the same time. The model recognizes that the interventions and strategies chosen influence each employee and the organization as a whole.

- Work@Health Program

  The CDC Work@Health Program is an employer-based training program focused on improving the health of participating employers, with an emphasis on reducing chronic disease and injury risk and improving worker productivity.

- Worksite Health Scorecard

  The CDC Worksite Health Scorecard is a tool designed to help employers assess if they are implementing science-based health promotion interventions in their worksites to prevent heart disease, stroke, and related health conditions such as hypertension, diabetes, and obesity.

The CDC encourages the use of effective workplace programs and policies to reduce health risks and improve quality of life for workers in America. Their goal is to educate on health promotion as it relates to the design, implementation, and evaluation of effective workplace health promotion programs.

Centers for Disease Control (CDC) – National Institute for Occupational Safety & Health (NIOSH)

According to their website, "The Occupational Safety and Health Act of 1970 established NIOSH as a research agency focused on the study of worker safety and health, and empowering employers and workers to create safe and healthy workplaces. It has the mandate to assure 'every man and woman in the Nation safe and healthful working conditions and to preserve our human resources.'"[33]

NIOSH promotes productive workplaces through safety and health research. I like to describe the NIOSH and their Total Worker Health program as the intersection of workplace safety with wellness or wellbeing. NIOSH's goals are outlined on their website as:

1. Conduct research to reduce worker illness and injury, and to advance worker well-being.
2. Promote safe and healthy workers through interventions, recommendations, and capacity building.
3. Enhance worker safety and health through global collaborations.

NIOSH conducts research programs to publish data and statistics for publications and products related to furthering their goals. NIOSH information can be especially beneficial when assisting manufacturing employers with their wellbeing goals, strategies, or programs. Quite often these organizations have very strong safety programs and adding wellbeing onto a safety program can help spread the wellbeing mission in a population that takes safety seriously.

"NIOSH's Total Worker Health® (TWH) is defined as policies, programs, and practices that integrate protection from work-related safety and health hazards with promotion of injury and illness prevention efforts to advance worker well-being. TWH is a holistic approach to worker well-being. It acknowledges risk factors related to work that contribute to health problems previously considered unrelated to work. The TWH approach seeks to improve well-being in the American workforce for the benefit of workers, employers, and the nation by protecting safety and enhancing health and productivity."[34]

Gallup

Gallup states on their website that they are "a global analytics and advice firm that helps leaders and organizations solve their most pressing problems."[35] Quite obviously, one of the most pressing issues any business faces is the cost of health care and the health and happiness of their workforce. Gallup assesses attitudes and behaviors of various groups of people, including employees, and analyzes this data so businesses can use it to transform their culture and workforce. They focus on challenges that human resources face, like developing, tracking, and retaining talent, building a great culture, employee engagement, performance management, manager and strengths development, diversity and inclusion, wellbeing, workforce analytics, and aligning strategy to the goals of the organization.

Gallup is very well known for their organizational surveys to employees and their finding that "Those who [have a best friend at work] are seven times as likely to be engaged in their jobs, are better at engaging customers, produce higher quality work, have higher well-being, and are less likely to get injured on the job. In sharp contrast, those without a best friend in the workplace have just a 1 in 12 chance of being engaged."[36]

Two of Gallup's employees, Tom Rath and Jim Harter, PhD, authored the book *Wellbeing: The Five Essential Elements*, which provides a holistic view of how one can achieve and maintain wellbeing throughout their lifetime. This book focuses on the five essential elements they believe to be most important:

1. Career wellbeing (also referred to as "purpose" by Gallup)
2. Social wellbeing
3. Financial wellbeing
4. Physical wellbeing
5. Community wellbeing

As a complement to the book, they also offer the use of the online Gallup tool Wellbeing Finder™ to assist in one's wellbeing journey.

Global Wellness Institute (GWI)

The Global Wellness Institute (GWI) describes itself as "a 501(c)(3) non-profit organization with a mission to empower wellness worldwide by educating the public and private sectors about preventative health and wellness." Their mission is to empower wellness organizations by facilitating collaboration, providing global research and insight, triggering innovation, and advocating for growth and sustainability.

"Through its five pillars—Research, Initiatives, Roundtable Discussions, wellnessevidence.com and The Wellness Moonshot™: A World Free of Preventable Disease—the GWI informs and connects key stakeholders capable of impacting the overall wellbeing of our planet and its citizens. The GWI makes all of its valuable information and resources available at no cost, which allows anyone, anywhere, access."[37]

The GWI has many global initiatives (23 listed on their website in 2019) that include topics like wellness tourism, wellness for children, wellness for cancer, sustainability, wellness architecture, mental wellness, social impact, healthy aging, digital wellness, beauty meets wellness, and wellness at work. While their wellness at work initiative is one of many, it is still worth following them and understanding their reports to get a better look at the industry at large.

State Organizations

Individual states have organizations as well. I spend much of my time in Michigan and sit on the board of two of our most prominent groups: the Michigan Wellness Council and the Best and Brightest in Wellness. I will share with you the details of those two groups, but you should research your specific state to find out if they have a wellness council or corporate wellness group you can become involved with.

Michigan Wellness Council (MWC)

The Michigan Wellness Council (MWC) is a "nonprofit organization whose vision is that the health and wellbeing of Michigan employers will be the best in the nation. We execute on this mission by inspiring the implementation of leading workplace wellness strategies through thought-leadership and education."[38]

This state wellness council is devoted to bringing national best-in-class education and thought leaders to the state of Michigan so employer wellbeing practitioners in the state can have affordable access to professional certification trainings and ideas that can be implemented in their workplace. This is achieved through public meetings, conferences, trainings, webinars, and podcasts. There are also many resources on their website, such as helpful links to many free resources, meeting resources, interviews, and a large library of books for purchase and information for download.

If you are lucky enough to have a state wellness council in your area, I highly recommend becoming involved. The annual membership fees are typically affordable, and the benefits are vast. The networking opportunities at the meetings and quality of education are by far worth the price of entry.

The Best and Brightest in Wellness

As described on their website, "The Best and Brightest in Wellness® is an innovative initiative that recognizes and celebrates quality and excellence in health awareness. This unique program highlights companies, schools, faith-based groups, and organizations that promote a culture of wellness; and those that plan, implement, and evaluate efforts in employee wellness to make their business and the community a healthier place to live and work. All companies, no matter what type, can be a Best and Brightest in Wellness® by building better business, creating richer lives, and growing stronger communities."[39]

The group facilitates a program to recognize and reward groups and organizations that excel in wellbeing. These awards are given at a one-day event focused on education in wellbeing and networking of Michigan employers who promote a healthy workplace.

Nomination and recognition programs help employers to understand how their wellbeing strategies and initiatives compare to best-in-class strategies and those of other organizations. While it is true that no two organizations are identical, completing benchmarking tools and surveys helps us understand what others are doing and sparks ideas and interest in new areas that may have been otherwise off our radar. It is a good practice to benchmark ourselves against others, and this group provides one of the many survey tools available for that.

Local and Community Support

In addition to national and state resources and organizations, there are many resources and types of support in most local communities for wellness activities or even possibly free assistance. These vary by community, but typically involve:

- County or City Resources
    - County speaker's bureau
    - Directories of physical activity opportunities (runs, walks, nonprofit events)
    - Health department services

- Health System, Hospital, and Health Plan Resources
    - Community outreach initiatives
    - Community events
    - Expert speakers
    - Medical initiatives, screenings, and immunizations

- College and University Resources
    - Speakers
    - Case study assistance

- Retail Resources
    - Bike/running shops, pharmacies, grocery stores, gyms, Weight Watchers, etc.

These resources are typically low cost or free, as these groups are either funded by their respective county or city or they are groups interested in promoting their services to an insured or wellbeing-minded population of employees. An employer wellbeing event is a free audience of insured employees that an expert health practitioner can basically advertise to. By offering a free presentation or screening to your employees, a physician is forming a relationship with insured individuals who are local to his/her office. By providing a free presentation on proper running techniques, a local running shop is promoting their service, expertise, and location to employees who are interested in their topic and might utilize their retail store for services. By providing onsite healthy cooking demos, a local healthy grocery store is highlighting their healthy choices and promoting to employees with interest. The key is realizing that employees are marketing assets to local vendors, practitioners, and other groups. However, an important consideration when utilizing these resources is if the employer has a non-solicitation of employee policy with such presenters or vendors. It is important to verify that employees may be solicited to before setting up an event with a vendor of this type.

Industry Authors and Experts

While many of the large books and studies in the industry have already been discussed in this chapter under their aforementioned organizations, there are a couple of individual authors/experts I would like to highlight so you know who they are and what their contributions have been.

First is Dee Edington, who is a pioneer in the employee health and wellbeing industry. Dee Edington, PhD, made a strong name for himself as the founder and a professor of the University of Michigan Health Management Research Center (UM HMRC) and was the director of the center until June 2011. The center has since closed, but Dee's impact on the industry remains strong.

He has authored two well-known books in the industry, *Zero Trends: Health as a Serious Economic Strategy* and *Shared Values-Shared Results: Positive Organizational Health as a Win-Win Philosophy* (co-author Jennifer S. Pitts PhD). He has focused on the employee health and wellbeing industry for decades. "Dr. Edington's research focuses on the precursors of disease and vitality. His interest is in the relationships between healthy lifestyles, vitality, and quality of life, as they benefit both individuals and organizations. He is specifically interested in how individual health management, worksite wellness activities, and programs within organizations impact health care cost containment, productivity, and human resource development."[40]

Dee's first book, *Zero Trends: Health as a Serious Economic Strategy*, gained much popularity in the industry due to its three key strategies recommended to reduce health care costs and improve productivity:

1. Keep healthy employees healthy
2. Create a culture of health
3. Don't get worse

Dee charts the typical progression of declining health/increased costs versus the flatlining costs (or "bending of the trend") of those engaged in health and wellbeing initiatives. These results are further broken down by three levels of engagement for companies (traditional, comprehensive, and champion companies). "Zero trends" (no health care cost increase over the five-year study) were only achieved by champion companies, but the trend followed with the two additional levels. This is why he recommends we "keep healthy employees healthy."

In the same vein is his recommendation to help employees "not get worse." He correlated the number of health risks employees have with their medical expenses and focused on risk transitions between the groups. It is easier to keep someone in the low risk group than move them back from medium risk. And it is easier to keep someone in medium risk than move them back from the high-risk group.

When working in this industry, you may encounter the discussion, maybe even in the form of pushback, about how only the "healthy employees participate in wellness programs or activities." The insinuation is that the employee would engage in that activity with or without you offering it, so why waste the company money. This book and these findings are valuable tools when educating our friends with this view.

Dr. Edington's research and books are widely known in the industry. Understanding the basics of both his books will help any employee health and wellbeing practitioner gain clarity on the industry, as well as show them to be a well-studied expert in the field. I highly recommend reviewing.

Another industry author and expert is Laura Putnam. Laura is the author of *Workplace Wellness that Works*, a book that helps readers shift the wellness conversation from one of implementing a wellness program to starting a wellness movement within their organization. In this book, Laura outlines ten actionable steps and tangible ways to impact employee health and happiness, promoting an overall culture of wellbeing. Some of these key steps include the following:

- Appeal to positive emotions instead of enforcing compliance.
- Shift the focus from improved health to improved quality of life.
- Tap into the power of intrinsic motivation over incentives.
- Use "nudges" and "cues" to make the healthy choice the easy choice.
- "Go stealth" — and "sneak" wellness into non-wellness initiatives.
- Integrate well-being into the fabric of business as usual.[41]

A particular area of focus of Laura's has been empowering managers to become "multipliers of well-being" (which is the topic for her next book). A growing body of research suggests that managers are best positioned to catalyze a population toward enhanced wellbeing. Following this philosophy, Laura conveys the importance of a manager's role in their team members' engagement with their work as well as their overall wellbeing. Her publications and workshops empower managers to take a more active and hands-on role by engaging in three simple practices: Do, Speak, Create.

- Do: Lead by example;
- Speak: Engage in conversation around wellbeing; and
- Create: Devise team-based systems and rituals to promote wellbeing within the construct of the team.

Laura assists managers in the reframing of wellness into a conversation that focuses on quality of life and support, while directing it away from compliance, incentives, and forcefulness. Health and happiness are profoundly personal topics and, for this reason, managers must learn how to motivate and inspire versus coerce and incentivize employees into workplace wellness program participation.

I strongly believe that all managers would be wise to integrate a workplace wellbeing strategy that supports employees' personal goals, health, and happiness, not only to support the health of their workforce but also their department and the bottom line of the organization. Laura is wonderful at educating and motivating managers to make positive changes in their managerial style and support around wellbeing. I highly recommend studying Laura's work and offering her resources to managers, as it is a very important piece of the employer wellbeing puzzle.

CHAPTER 8

DEFINING GOALS AND
MEASURING RESULTS

One of the most common errors I see in the corporate wellness industry is the lack of a strategy and a definition of success, especially in the smaller employer market. Since the wellness or wellbeing programs are often being administered by human resource professionals as an added task, they are expected to do this above and beyond their normal work duties. This is difficult and creates a situation where the person responsible for the wellness program might not be an expert in the space. They probably know enough to be dangerous but have not studied best-in-class practices, don't belong to organizations that are publishing research and putting on the national conferences, nor have they been exposed to successful programs or even understand how to define success.

It wasn't until I became involved with some of the national organizations that I truly started to understand the best-in-class practices and research. Before that, I didn't understand how to set a strategy, which includes thoughtfully identifying a wellness program's mission, vision, goals, or success metrics, as well as outlining the tactical processes by which an organization can achieve these goals.

As a holistic practitioner and author of a book on mind, body, spirit integration, I knew a holistic look at wellness (what we call wellbeing) was necessary to achieve true health, and I understood intuitively what worked and what did not with changing behavior. But I didn't know how to put that into a strategy until I started studying the world of employer benefits and those organizations leading the research in this space.

Focusing on how to set strategy and goals will help us better understand what is necessary for success within corporations' wellness strategies. Setting and measuring goals is important whenever we make change, no matter if this is an individual change or a change we want to make within a corporation. Let's first look at the various goals a corporation could be trying to achieve with a wellness or wellbeing program or strategy:

- Reduce Employee Turnover
- Increase Employee Engagement
- Increase Employee Attraction
- Improve Employee Recruitment
- Increase Employee Referrals
- Retain Talent
- Reduce Absenteeism
- Increase Productivity
- Increase Employee Energy Levels
- Increase Employee Job Satisfaction
- Increase Employee Morale
- Increase Comradery
- Help Employees Find Work/Life Balance
- Help Employees Find Purpose/Meaning
- Connect Employees to Each Other
- Connect Employees to Community
- Improve Employee Physical Health
- Improve Employee Mental Health
- Improve Employee Financial Health
- Improve Employee Emotional Health
- Increase Team Effectiveness
- Improve Business Operations and Efficiency
- Improve Business Performance

- Improve Business Profitability
- Grow Revenue
- Increase Quality
- Increase Customer Satisfaction
- Reduce Worker's Compensation Claims
- Improve Risk Management
- Reduce Safety Incidents
- Improve Safety Metrics
- Reduce 401K Loans
- Increase Preventive Exam Rates
- Increase Preventive Screenings Rates
- Increase Employee Happiness
- Reduce Health Care Costs
- Reduce ER Use for Non-Emergent Care
- Help Employees Pay Off Debt
- Help Employees Retire
- Help Employees Survive Emergencies Financially
- Help Employees Achieve a Better Lifestyle
- Help Employees Pay for Education
- Help Employees with Stable Income
- Help Employees Pay Mortgage/Rent

These are just a few examples, and if you think back to the lists of ROI and VOI, you'll notice those are basically a list of the goals a corporation could have for implementing a wellness program. As we discussed in that chapter, some of the VOIs (Value on Investment) are difficult to measure, while the ROIs (Return on Investment) are easier to measure because they are driven more by numbers or dollars.

Identifying the goals of a wellness strategy must not be completed by the one person responsible for wellness alone. Doing so would

THE EMPLOYEE WELLBEING HANDBOOK

not take into account all the stakeholders of an organization and what is best for the corporation as a whole. If it is possible to involve various stakeholders and chief level officers in this process, not only will buy-in to the wellness strategy be accomplished more rapidly, but the goals will be a true reflection of the organization's business priorities. This will allow the wellness or wellbeing initiatives to infiltrate the culture of the organization, rather than being a silo program.

As well, this will give the person responsible for wellness or wellbeing a seat at the executive's table, allowing them to interact with the chief level officers, managers, and directors in setting corporate strategy. Communicating the value of the wellbeing strategy to all stakeholders will involve them in the process and help the entire organization take ownership of the wellbeing goals and supporting tactical programs.

It is important to keep the wellness goals to a minimum, especially when beginning a program. While all corporations would like to see all measures of VOI and ROI improve, choosing three to five goals will keep the task manageable and realistic.

It is also important, once those three to five goals are chosen, that a way to measure each goal is decided upon and then annually reported so you know if the intervention is making an impact. Below are some examples of how to measure goals and who to work with to attain this data.

- Improve Business Profitability
  - How: This can be measured using annual profit numbers
  - With Whom: Accounting Department

- Improve Business Operations and Efficiency
  - How: This can be measured using operation targets and production numbers
  - With Whom: Operations Department

112

- Grow Revenue
  - How: This can be measured using sales numbers
  - With Whom: Sales Department

- Increase Quality
  - How: This can be measured using number of defective product or reworked product
  - With Whom: Quality Department

- Increase Customer Satisfaction
  - How: This can be measured using sales numbers
  - With Whom: Sales or Customer Service Department

- Reduce Absenteeism
  - How: This can be measured using absenteeism data (if not a lumped PTO policy)
  - With Whom: Human Resource Department

- Reduce Worker's Comp Claims
  - How: This can be measured using worker compensation claim information
  - With Whom: Risk Management, Safety, or Human Resource Departments

- Reduce Safety Incidents
  - How: This can be measured using safety incident logs and numbers
  - With Whom: Safety or Human Resource Department

- Reduce Employee Turnover/ Increase Employee Attraction, Recruitment, and Referrals
  - How: This can be measured using employee hiring and termination data
  - With Whom: Human Resource Department

- Reduce 401K Loans/ Improve Employee Financial Health
  - How: This can be measured using data from the retirement plan or vendor
  - With Whom: Benefits or Human Resource Department

- Increase Preventive Exam/Screening Rates
  - How: This can be measured using data from the health plan or vendor (year-end report)
  - With Whom: Benefits or Human Resource Department

- Reduce Health Care Costs/ ER Use for Non-emergent Care
  - How: This can be measured using data from the health plan or vendor (year-end report)
  - With Whom: Benefits or Human Resource Department

Some goals are very difficult to measure. Regardless, if the goal is important enough to the corporation to be in the top five, it should be included. In these cases, employee surveys, health risk assessments, or cultural assessments can be helpful to measure the goal. Examples of these types of goals are:

- Increase Employee Energy Levels
- Help Employees Find Work/Life Balance
- Help Employees Find Purpose/Meaning
- Help Employees Achieve a Better Lifestyle
- Help Employees Feel Safe
- Connect Employees to Each Other
- Connect Employees to Community
- Increase Employee Job Satisfaction
- Increase Employee Morale
- Increase Comradery
- Increase Team Effectiveness
- Improve Employee Physical Health

- Improve Employee Mental Health
- Improve Employee Emotional Health
- Increase Employee Engagement
- Increase Employee Happiness

Utilizing the above concepts, you can start to understand what goals are important to an organization. Once the goals are known and the measurement data is identified, the tactics that will help the organization achieve those goals can be implemented. There are enough examples to fill a whole book, so we will limit this to only a few. This is where a seasoned consultant can offer valuable guidance. Some examples of tactics to achieve certain goals are:

1. Goal: Reduce Absenteeism

- Tactical Program Ideas:
  - Implement a wellbeing program during cold and flu season, possibly incentivizing employees to participate
    - Educate employees about how to lessen the spread of germs
      - Hand-washing techniques
      - Proper coughing practices
      - Sanitizing common workspaces, machines, offices, conference rooms, telephones, monitors, keyboards, etc.
      - Wearing face masks or staying home when sick
      - No handshaking policy when sick or during cold/ flu season
      - Work with maintenance to make sure air filters are regularly changed
      - Proper dish/cup/mug/utensil washing and clean sponges in workplace kitchens
    - Flu vaccinations

- Immune booster education programs
  - Supplemental support
  - The importance of sleep on health
  - How to eat to support the immune system
- Promotional campaigns (emails, posters, home mailers, etc.)

2. Goal: Increase Preventive Exam/Screening Rates

- Tactical Program Ideas:
  - Implement an employee campaign around annual PCP (Primary Care Physician) visits
    - Educate employees on ACA no-cost preventive care services
    - Educate employees on how to find and select a PCP who is covered under their health plan network and is in line with their personal health goals
    - Educate employees on the importance of annual screenings and how even at a young age, this creates a baseline for the future
    - Educate employees on how early disease detection could dramatically improve health outcomes
    - Incentivize employees to see their PCP annually
    - Incentivize employees to get their age/gender-appropriate screenings (pap smear, mammogram, colonoscopy, PSA [prostate], dental, vision, dermatology, bone density, etc.)
    - Bring physicians onsite for specific visits or screenings
    - Bring mobile units onsite for various screenings (mammogram, cardiogram, etc.)

3. Goal: Help Employees Lose Weight

- Tactical Program Ideas:
  - Incentivize employees to participate or achieve goal
  - Bring in weight loss programs, like Weight Watchers at Work
  - Create a group challenge, like Biggest Loser
  - Engage health plan to offer weight loss resources
    - Digital or onsite challenges
    - Telephonic or onsite coaching
  - Help employees increase their activity levels
    - Create various group challenges
      - Walking challenges
      - Wearable tracker challenges
      - Fitness challenges
      - Yoga challenges
      - Cardio challenges
    - Bring fitness classes onsite so employees can try them
    - Engage local gyms/studios for free passes for employees
    - Set up group classes at various fitness/yoga studios locally
    - Reimburse for gym or fitness/yoga studios for employees
  - Harness the power around New Year's resolutions
  - Set up various nutrition programs
    - Onsite education presentations
    - Cooking demos
    - Smoothie bars
  - Organize healthy food options onsite

- If onsite cafeteria, coordinate healthy food options or even subsidize healthy options
- Create a list of healthy restaurants or food items at nearby restaurants
- Request healthy foods be added to vending machines
- Look at customs in workplace that might be bringing unhealthy foods into the workplace and find a way to add healthy options
  - Monthly birthday celebrations might have cake and ice cream – add fruit to the celebration
  - Bagel Friday should also have vegetable sticks and dip
  - If lunch room has free snacks, make sure free fruit or other healthy options are also available
- Create a list of acceptable foods if vendors bring in treats for your staff and make a policy to distribute to any entity trying to feed staff

As you can see, for each goal, there are many possible ideas for tactical programs that can help the organization achieve their goal. This is all part of the larger wellbeing strategy and is important to give serious consideration to. Certain programs will work better, or not at all, for certain populations. It depends upon the organizations' employee demographic, geographic location, budget, culture, type of business, and industry. If the strategy, goals, tactical program, and areas of focus are not carefully designed, it could ultimately mean the program fails. It is important to take the time to carefully craft a strategy, realize the metrics by which to measure success, and annually reevaluate the program to determine its success.

Typically, a strategy is best built as a three- to five-year plan. This allows a roadmap to be created that adds each year, slowly introducing the concept and building the culture of health and wellness.

If a company starts too quickly or does not have a strategy, typically the program will fizzle out. If thoughtfully crafted, the organization will take baby steps, slowly bringing the employees on a wellness or wellbeing journey. Each year, the strategy can be revisited, engaging more stakeholders in the discussion. These stakeholders can be internal (employees, managers, directors, C-suite, board of directors) or external (wellness/wellbeing vendors, EAPs, health plan, benefit brokers, community resources, government entities). If the goals are being realized, this will build a strong case for more funding. If the goals are not being realized, either the goals were too aggressive or the wrong tactical programs were chosen.

When evaluating the successes year over year, questions to ask are:

- What were participation rates?
- Why did the employees not participate?
- Did we communicate the programs effectively to the employees?
- Did we offer incentives?
- Were the incentives substantial enough? (Keep in mind laws exist around amounts.)
- What was the employee feedback?
- Were there any major success stories/employee testimonials?
- What would have made the employees more interested?
- Were the employees ready to make the change? (Readiness for change discussion.)
- Did we realize any ROI?
- Did we realize any VOI?
- Did we assist in creating a culture of health and wellbeing?
- Where else could we spend our budget for a higher ROI/VOI?
- Have we surveyed employees to know what they liked/did not like about the program?

- If we used heavy incentives, how did we move from extrinsic to intrinsic motivation?
- How do we tell a story with the strategy – incorporating various data points into the discussion?

Combining data from all the various vendors can be very difficult, depending on the size of the employer, the data available to them, and the budget they have available for a portal. This can be very difficult to do unless the employer is very large (with similar budget). However, it is certainly possible. Again, this is where an experienced consultant can be valuable for their ability to look at various vendor reports and tell a story of success.

CHAPTER 9

SUCCESS THROUGH COLLABORATION (CONCLUSION)

In this book, you have learned about the wellness industry from various angles. You have learned about the shift from wellness to wellbeing and the various areas of focus within wellbeing. You've learned about culture, the benefit industry as it relates to wellness, pricing models, and the various kinds of vendors. You have learned important terminology and acronyms, legal information, who the industry influencers are, and how to define goals. Hopefully, you have also read between the lines and gleaned ideas about industry collaboration, within the benefit vendor industry and within an organization itself.

We have all heard the axiom, "Even illness becomes wellness when 'I' is replaced with 'we.'" And it's true! It takes an entire support system to achieve maximum health and wellbeing for employees. Collaborations across all departments and professional disciplines are necessary if we want to truly impact the health of our employees. Wellness is not about contracting a vendor. Wellness is about organizing the entire workplace to support health. Wellness is about building the workplace infrastructure with health in mind. Wellness is about making every business decision with the impact on employee and community health and wellbeing—not just the bottom line of the company—as a top consideration.

At the end of the day, we all want to be happy and healthy. The employee wellbeing industry is just a manifestation of that wish for a larger group of people. Altruism is sometimes a company's main goal for their wellbeing strategy. A wellbeing strategy goal doesn't have to be related to productivity or profit levels. If a company can afford to improve their employees' lives, they often do, for no other reason than they believe it is the right thing to do. There is nothing greater management can do than set up their workplace to support health and happiness. We must design health and happiness into our lives. It is far easier to do this than to force anyone into behavior change.

America is a tough place to be an employee. Unlike other nations, which focus on shorter work weeks, midday breaks, national paid parental leave, laws governing work/life balance, and mandatory annual leave time, it is the norm (and legal) for American businesses to focus on productivity and profit before all else. Overworking and underpaying our employees has become the norm. We have eliminated the societal duty of keeping work to manageable hours. Employees who are caregivers (to their elderly parents, their children, or both) are stretched to the limit, and our society has little support to offer. Unfortunately, American cultural values focus too much on material success and money and not enough on passion, fun, travel, time with family and friends, purpose, life satisfaction, our social network, and community—all the things that foster true happiness.

Research suggests that we cannot chase happiness, but instead must set up our surroundings to support happiness. I love the idea of helping people design happiness into their lives and helping companies design happiness into their workplaces. To do this, we need to consider what makes people truly happy. As mentioned in chapter 1 of this book, the Blue Zone Project (www.BlueZones.com) focuses on how to set up an environment to support the health and happiness of people living in that environment. Their focus is on places people live and how we can support the development and implementation of governmental policy. But the same is true for workplaces. We need to design the workplace to support health and happiness. We need to support the American worker in their ability to find satisfaction in their lives, know their purpose, eat well, and sleep enough. We need to encourage vacations and time away from work so workers can recharge. We need to help American workers connect to their joy and help them build relationships with each other. As Gallup has taught us, the most important indicator of someone's happiness in their job is if they have a best friend at work.

We are social beings who need to socialize with other people for maximized happiness. We need to feel a sense of community and, for most working Americans, the only opportunity for this is in the workplace. So, how do we set up the workplace to maximize profitability and socialization? How do we help American workers learn to love their jobs and connect to their work? We all know healthy, happy employees are better employees (productive, balanced, cooperative, etc.) even if it's difficult to measure. Leaders in touch with their higher consciousness know this intuitively, but wellness strategies can help define and execute this vision. They help create a culture that supports health. Creating a wellness or wellbeing strategy that guides a corporation toward a more supportive and humane work environment will pay dividends in the long run.

According to a survey conducted by Wrike, which is discussed in the report "From Positivity to Productivity: Exposing the Truth Behind Workplace Happiness," compensation, flexible hours, and doing meaningful work are the top contributing factors to happiness. The same survey indicates that the "majority of the happiest employees in the United States, United Kingdom, and Germany all rank 'doing meaningful work' as the #1 factor for happiness, over both 'compensation' and 'flexible hours.'" In fact, "In the U.S. specifically, meaningful work is especially important to happiness. Over half (58 percent) of full-time U.S. employees say they've taken a pay cut to accept a job that made them happier at work."[42]

Happy employees are simply more productive. According to Wrike's study, American employees who describe their happiness levels as "elated" lead productivity charts with 91 percent reporting they're "very productive." Happy employees make the workplace better for everyone. They are more cooperative and helpful, are 4 percent better at customer service, commit 26 percent fewer clinical errors, exhibit 79 percent lower burnout, and have a 61 percent lower probability of leaving their employer than unhappy employees.[43]

I am challenging all of us to look at wellbeing as an opportunity to build and implement a happy and healthy culture within our organizations. Where can we "slide wellness in?" How can we systematically weave wellbeing into the fabric of the organization? How can we constantly remember to consider employee health and happiness when creating new company policies and procedures? In what way can we support employees who are in low-, high-, and medium-risk health pools? In what way can we support employees who are not as happy as they could be? What types of benefits will help employees most and how do we engage employees in the benefits offered? How do we educate employees so they understand what benefits are right for them and know how to use their benefits properly?

It is a complex solution at best and requires the collaboration of many. Until our nation makes worker wellbeing a priority and develops legislation to further support it, it is the job of each employer to make the internal policies and procedure changes to support employees.

As I mentioned in the book's opening, my goal with this book was to help all who read this gain the knowledge to deploy a successful wellbeing strategy and comprehensive approach in any employer environment. You should now have an understanding of the wellness landscape and where you or your business can best fit in. I am extremely grateful for all who work in the wellness field and choose to better the lives of others. Quite often, someone enters this field because of a personal passion and, just like happiness is contagious, so is passion and purpose. I am excited for you to disseminate your newfound knowledge and tools to create a better workplace environment for all. I appreciate and applaud your efforts.

THANK YOU FOR READING

Thank you for reading this book.

If you want to learn more, or to connect with me, please visit my company's website here: https://www.synbella.com/, or connect with me on my personal site here: https://www.cassiesobelton.com/

I appreciated that you choose to go on this learning journey with me.

I can't wait to hear from you!

-Cassie

A QUICK FAVOR PLEASE?

Before you go, I would like to ask a favor of you please.

Would you be so kind as to leave this book a review on Amazon?

Reviews are very important for authors. Not only do they help us to write more books, they also give potential readers insights into how the book will help them.

Please take a minute and leave this book an honest review. Share what you liked, what you didn't like, and any thoughts on how the book helped you personally or professionally.

It doesn't take very long (even just a few sentences would be appreciated!), but it can help this book reach more readers.

Thank you again for reading, and thank you so much for your time helping with the review,

-Cassie

ABOUT THE AUTHOR

Cassie Sobelton is an expert in the field of personal and employee wellbeing. As a frequent contributor to numerous media outlets, she has educated business leaders, employees and the public by way of spokesperson roles, recurring news segments, a health and wellness podcast, a variety of print features, recurrent radio shows, various webinars and frequent keynote addresses.

Sobelton believes in a real world approach to Mind, Body, Spirit balance. Her first book, *Back to Balance: Crack Your Mind, Body, Spirit Code to Transform Your Health*, was a #1 Best Seller that tackled individual health and wellness. Through SynBella and her new book, *The Employee Wellbeing Handbook: A Guide for Collaboration Across All Departments, Benefit Vendors and Health Practitioners to Build a Culture of Wellness Within Any Organization*, she is turning her attention to corporate wellbeing. SynBella was founded in 2011 after Sobelton experienced a major health scare and subsequent full recovery. Through this experience, she learned the value of a healthy mind and body, and today, she brings that knowledge to others through speaking, writing and consulting.

Sobelton's background encompasses a unique fusion of employee wellbeing experience that distinguishes her as a balanced leader who implements her diverse knowledge and experience with successful results. Leading employee wellbeing initiatives at a health system, health plan, benefit broker and traditional wellness vendor, Sobelton understands the various stakeholder's positions, needs and goals, allowing for a complete view of the wellbeing industry.

Sobelton exudes a passion for wellness that she effectively uses to achieve her professional, personal and client goals. Ms. Sobelton lives a spiritual and active life filled with friends, family, exercise, biking, kayaking, practicing Eastern philosophies, and daily gratitude.

ENDNOTES

1   https://news.gallup.com/poll/245873/seven-maintain-negative-view-heal thcare-system.aspx

2   https://www.kornferry.com/institute/workplace-stress-motivation

3   https://www.ncbi.nlm.nih.gov/pmc/articles/PMC3341916/

4   A.H. Maslow, "A theory of human motivation," *Psychological Review, 50*(4) (1943): 370-396.

5   Dan Buettner, "Power 9® Reverse Engineering Longevity," Blue Zones, accessed June 25, 2019, https://www.bluezones.com/2016/11/power-9/.

6   "5 'Blue Zones' Where the World's Healthiest People Live," National Geographic, April 6, 2017, accessed on 6/25/19, https://www.nationalgeographic .com/books/features/5-blue-zones-where-the-worlds-healthiest-people-live/.

7   "5 'Blue Zones' Where the World's Healthiest People Live," National Geographic, April 6, 2017, accessed on 6/25/19, https://www.nationalgeographic .com/books/features/5-blue-zones-where-the-worlds-healthiest-people-live/.

8   Dan Buettner, "Power 9® Reverse Engineering Longevity," Blue Zones, accessed June 25, 2019, https://www.bluezones.com/2016/11/power-9/.

9   "Workplace," Gallup, May 26, 1999, http://news.gallup.com/businessjour nal/511/item-10-best-friend-work.aspx.

10   Metlife's 15th Annual U.S. Employee Benefit Trends Study 2017 – https:// benefittrends.metlife.com/media/1382/2017-ebts-report_0320_exp0518_v2 .pdf

11   Consumer Financial Protection Bureau Financial Wellness at Work Report, 2014, accessed 6/25/19, https://www.greenpath.com/wp-content/up loads/2019/01/CFPB_ADA_compliant.pdf.

12   Stress in America Survey, 2015, p.7, American Psychological Association, accessed 6/25/19, https://www.apa.org/news/press/releases/stress/2014/stre ss-report.pdf.

13   Metlife's 17th Annual U.S. Employee Benefit Trends Study 2019, accessed 6/25/19, https://www.metlife.com/content/dam/metlifecom/us/ebts/pdf/Met Life-Employee-Benefit-Trends-Study-2019.pdf.

14   PricewaterhouseCoopers Employee Financial Wellness Survey 2018 Results, accessed 6/25/19, https://www.pwc.com/us/en/private-company-ser vices/publications/assets/pwc-2018-employee-wellness-survey.pdf.

15   PricewaterhouseCoopers Employee Financial Wellness Survey 2018 Results, accessed 6/25/19, https://www.pwc.com/us/en/private-company-services/publications/assets/pwc-2018-employee-wellness-survey.pdf.

16   Metlife's 17th Annual U.S. Employee Benefit Trends Study 2019, accessed 6/25/19, https://www.metlife.com/content/dam/metlifecom/us/ebts/pdf/MetLife-Employee-Benefit-Trends-Study-2019.pdf.

17   Dan Kadlec, "Proof That Workplace Financial Education Works," July 19, 2012, accessed on 6/25/19, http://business.time.com/2012/07/19/new-evidence-says-workplace-financial-education-effective/,

18   PricewaterhouseCoopers Employee Financial Wellness Survey 2018 Results, accessed 6/25/19,

https://www.pwc.com/us/en/private-company-services/publications/assets/pwc-2018-employee-wellness-survey.pdf.

19   Metlife's 15th Annual U.S. Employee Benefit Trends Study 2017, accessed 6//25/19, https://benefittrends.metlife.com/media/1382/2017-ebts-report_0320_exp0518_v2.pdf.

20   "Financial Wellness in the Workplace," SHRM, May 14, 2014, accessed 6/25/19, https://www.shrm.org/hr-today/trends-and-forecasting/research-and-surveys/pages/2014-financial-wellness.aspx.

21   Nancy Haught, "Seventh-day Adventists' Health Guidelines, Longevity Still Powerful Draw," May 8, 2012, accessed on 7/7/2019, https://www.oregonlive.com/living/2012/05/seventh-day_adventists_health.html

22   Dee W. Edington PhD, *Zero Trends: Health as a Serious Economic Strategy*, (Ann Arbor, MI: Health Management Research Center, 2009).

23   Global Wellness Economy Monitor, 2018 – Global Wellness Institute, Accessed 6/25/19, https://globalwellnessinstitute.org/wp-content/uploads/2019/04/GWIWellnessEconomyMonitor2018_042019.pdf

24   https://www.reginfo.gov/public/do/eAgendaViewRule?pubId=201904&RIN=3046-AB10

25   National Institute of Diabetes and Digestive and Kidney Diseases, accessed June 25, 2019, https://www.niddk.nih.gov/about-niddk/research-areas/diabetes/diabetes-prevention-program-dpp

26   National Institute of Diabetes and Digestive and Kidney Diseases, accessed June 25, 2019, https://www.niddk.nih.gov/about-niddk/research-areas/diabetes/diabetes-prevention-program-dpp

27   https://hero-health.org/

28   https://www.nationalwellness.org/

29   https://www.welcoa.org

30   https://www.artsciencehpi.com

31   https://www.businessgrouphealth.org

32   https://www.cdc.gov/workplacehealthpromotion/index.html

33   https://www.cdc.gov/niosh/index.htm

34   https://www.cdc.gov/niosh/twh/default.html

35   https://www.gallup.com/

36   https://news.gallup.com/businessjournal/127043/friends-social-wellbe
ing.aspx

37   https://globalwellnessinstitute.org/

38   http://www.michiganwellnesscouncil.org

39   https://thebestandbrightest.com/events/michigans-2019-best-and-brigh
test-in-wellness/

40   http://edingtonassociates.com/

41   https://www.motioninfusion.com/about.html

42   "From Positivity to Productivity: Exposing the Truth Behind Workplace
Happiness," Wrike, p. 7, https://cdn.wrike.com/ebook/From_Positivity_to_Pro
ductivity_Exposing+the+Truth_Behind_Workplace_Happiness.pdf

43   "From Positivity to Productivity: Exposing the Truth Behind Workplace
Happiness," Wrike, p. 3, https://cdn.wrike.com/ebook/From_Positivity_to_Pro
ductivity_Exposing+the+Truth_Behind_Workplace_Happiness.pdf

Made in the USA
Columbia, SC
21 December 2019